YESTERDAY'S HARVEST

Brian Carter

Illustrated by the author

Best Wishes,
Brian Carter

Torbay Books
7 Torquay Road   Paignton   Devon TQ3 3DU

By the same author

A Black Fox Running

Lundy's War

The Moon in the Weir

Jack

In the Long Dark

Nightworld

Where the Dream Begins

Walking in the Wild

Carter Country

First published 1982 J.M. Dent and Sons Ltd.
Republished 2005 Torbay Books
Copyright © 2005 Text and illustrations: Brian Carter

Printed for Torbay Books
7 Torquay Road, Paignton, Devon TQ3 3DU

Contents

To my mother
and father

Nature never did betray the heart that loved her
William Wordsworth

1

The Dancing Fox

Suddenly the sky was empty. The swifts that had filled it the evening before were gone, mysteriously, and the dew lay longer on the grass and the sun moved more hurriedly across the day. There was a feeling, too, that summer would soon follow the birds south, leaving a sadness in the air and in the corners of the heart. For the end of summer was a kind of death and all the stubble fires blurring the hillsides with gold could not delay the slide into darkness.

But then Mam sat at the table by the shaded lamp, her shadow huge on the blind, her golden face soft with the love of me, juggling the words, making the word pictures grow behind my eyes. Her gentle voice and Welsh accent lapped at the margins of my consciousness, sending images like wavelets rippling from the pages of the Mabinogion.

" 'And this is how Arthur hunted the stag. They apportioned the hunting stations for the men and dogs, and loosed the dogs upon it; and the last dog that was loosed upon it was Arthur's favourite dog. Cafall was his name.' "

Beyond the green, sparkling Wales of mythology where I hunted beside King Arthur the moths ticked and thudded against the window and the craneflies tip-toed in grotesque slow motion along the picture rail. I was a small, blond, wiry nine-year-old and it was August of 1946. A crop of new names had been added to the little cenotaph in Palace Avenue, all the war dead of the town assembled alphabetically between the two dates, 1939–1945. When a tree is cut down it leaves a gap in the sky; when a neighbour dies he leaves an emptiness in the community, and I always felt autumn was a kind of adagio for lost things and lost people. It was the season of hiraeth, as the Welsh say, using the dusk word that is layered with many delicate flavours of sadness. To fall through hiraeth was to drift down fathoms of grief until a face rose to meet you or a landscape re-assembled and the ache subsided.

Now I could feel summer slipping away from me. Its breath blancoed the spiders' lace of morning and without the swifts the evenings were silent. But it was easy to be melancholy at night in the little back room of our brick terrace house on the outskirts of Paignton. Later the cats would sing their challenges from the tin roofs of the garden sheds and the tawny owl would flop into the horse chestnut tree and catch the stars in its big black eyes. The dewy air made the whole star field tremble and twinkle above the chimney pots, and there were no black shapes of German bombers droning overhead anymore, and the gas lamps shone in the streets and Mrs Williams across the way had not bothered to lower her blind.

I stood at my bedroom window wondering what went on in the smoke of day's end. I would remain perfectly still watching the glow lifting from the bottom of the sky while Nibs, our she-cat, dragged her black sleekness against my legs. Beyond the rooftops the last of the gulls straggled home and I knew God was waiting on the other side of darkness to hand out the brand new wellingtons and the Irish Wolf Hound and the powerful binoculars. And perhaps he would let me get hold of Beryl Eccles's tits which poked from the front of her frock like little apples. After death everything was possible provided you let God know what you wanted in your prayers.

My Sunday School God lived in Clennon Valley and spoke English with a broad Devon accent. All I had to do was run down Fisher Street past the Big Tree and up Dartmouth Road, through Tanner's Lane allotments and I was there. Aldebaran, Sirius, Aquila, the constellations of Pisces and Aries, the flaring silver stream of the Milky Way paved the path to infinity. But paradise was only a couple of streets distant where the houses ended and the brook rushed out of the wood singing its bright music to the hills.

Once at my window I heard a curlew calling high on its flight over the terrace, and it was the most beautiful and loneliest of sounds. From the living poetry I could construct fantasies of great estuarine places fit for heroes like Mr Mumford the insurance man who was killed at Dunkirk. And of course I had to create Nirvana for the pets and the wild creatures. Somewhere far off, even further south than Start Point, was the Avalon of birds and animals, and I was the only boy permitted to visit it. All the otters and red deer stags called me Bri and taught me how to speak their language.

God presided over the dreamscapes, an immense white light-house of a figure shining at world's end, surrounded by foxes and badgers and capering hares. His halo of golden songbirds was twice the size of the rings of Saturn. But until I became an Avalon resident Clennon Valley would do. I knew every spinney, copse, wood, orchard, farm, stream and lane. The sheep, cows and horses were my friends; the foxes were my comrades. Somehow the place and the creatures belonged to the Mabinogion. They had eluded the laws of physics and were magical and timeless like the fabric of a mirage. Lanes seemed to lead from nowhere to nowhere, and I would come upon derelict houses surrounded by tall, decaying Lawson Cypresses and hedges of macrocarpa. The shards of these experiences would break through the crust of Mam's storytelling: a little girl lifting the muslin curtains of a cottage window and smiling at me; huge horses chivvying the hedgerow grass, the roar of starlings above stubble; wet glinting farmland blotted with gulls. Things happened slowly with a curious, measured hush, and from the top of Cider Mill Hill the South Devon farmland ran to horizons whose lure had me choking on excitement.

A baffling presence lurked among the trees and hedges. It was capable of goosepimpling my flesh despite its obvious and enduring goodness. Celtic gods congregated in the mists of dimpsey by the flags of the pond at Waterside which was known locally as Pucksbog after an incident concerning an imp. Apparently the mischievous creature annoyed the devil and had his arse set on fire, but he managed to douse the flames by dunking his cheeks in the pond. How those animal-headed immortals must have guffawed and snorted at the spectacle. Perhaps it even got a chuckle out of Jehovah, although the Sunday School portraits showed him looking painfully stern and bearded in his nightshirt, like a Victorian undertaker modelling a shroud.

Dreamily I found myself trying to picture God's gigantic willie. Before I was chucked out of Sunday School for indecently exposing myself to the little girls, the red-faced young lady teacher who seemed to have access to heaven's secret files said God didn't have a willie, which struck me as odd. Odd willie-less God, the divine white-bearded undertaker-cum-gardener, planting acorns, ordering the tide to come in and go out, drawing stars on the sky with magic, phosphorescent paint.

"Why hasn't God got a willie, Mam?"

'Well, he don't drink and if you don't drink you don't go to the lav. So what would God want with a willie?"

Her logic impressed me but the Sunday School teacher could not be persuaded to continue the discussion.

"You're just rude, Carter," one of the girls said. "God will pay you back. My mum says you'll grow up like your dad – always in pubs drinking scrumpy with the devil. God don't like rude words."

"Bum and willie to God," I growled.

"You wouldn't say that if he was here."

"He is here. He's everywhere," Beryl Eccles said solemnly. Six and a half days a week she swore like a stoker and was far from saintly. Her sexual precociousness fed greedily on a passion for her own body and its potential as an instrument for pleasure. She had a round, plump freckly face, green eyes and lustrous brown hair flowing loose.

"God don't go down the pub, though," I said, "or he'd know my dad."

Learning about the Holy Land and the boring baby Moses and the Children of Israel who kept getting the thunderbolt treatment whenever they stepped out of line was purgatory on hot Sunday afternoons in the church hall. "It's more fun in hell," Dad said. "Heaven don't have any chip shops or off-sales. It's full of glum buggers singing hymns and praying and swigging tea."

Demonstrating total contempt for eternity he had time to note the fall of leaves, and sunsets and other worthless things like spring dawns, larksong and the loveliness of cows. What was to be did not hold his spirit hostage although he claimed he could read the ciphers of winter's starry skies. His life was not a mere rehearsal for death and he saw with the heart and possessed an inextinguishable optimism.

Dad's Valhalla will be an eternal Friday night of pub-crawling in boozy company. He lived for Fridays and not once can I recall him coming home from work early enough or sober enough to eat his dinner. He was a master carpenter who should have been the dictator of a banana republic where crazy, benign despotism is really appreciated. Mam was often irritated but never bored by his Walter Mitty lies and his sudden flights from terrace life.

"Wanted," he would say, pretending to read aloud from the *Paignton Observer*, "companion for alcoholic millionaire. Gents in their mid-forties are invited to apply for this highly desirable position. Intelligent, musically gifted boozers eager to earn £2,000 per annum should write at once to Bertie Bumwhistle the second, La-di-dah House, Toffy Nose Avenue, New York."

"Bloody fool!" Mam would snort. "Grow up, man. What must the boy think?"

In the face of his irresponsibility she exercised marvellous restraint born of loyalty and a curious fiery devotion. Her life was hard and how frustrated she must have been trying to express herself in scrubbed steps, polishing and dusting the house and cooking meals. See, cried those little acts of kindness which we took for granted, I think of you, I make things easy for you. What depths of maternal love are concealed beneath the trivia of family life where self-sacrifice so often goes unnoticed and unrewarded.

Between her Mabinogion and his building site Decameron arched the rainbow of my nights and days in Clennon Valley – the dream world bounded by adult dreams. But even at that age I had a taste for rough cider and port. Both my parents were pubby; Dad obsessively, Mam occasionally but always on a Saturday when there was singing and darts and explosive get-togethers with friends and neighbours. In those days the local was the haunt of farmworkers, roadmen, building labourers, craftsmen, shop assistants, fishermen and representatives of practically every other act of the roaring circus known loosely as the Working Class.

The Friday night pub blazed with Renaissance warmth and

colour. Whippets and border collies, lurchers, Jack Russells and mongrels lay before the fire, their paws caked with mud and cow dung. Maybe a couple of harled rabbits hung from the mantelpiece and Donkey Daniels – the town character and owner of the seaside donkeys – would be sitting, gaitered legs extended and boots cocked on the fender, gazing through his rough cider into the flames.

Beer and cider liberated a whole generation from drudgery and Dad's motto was: *horas non numero nisi serenas* ("I count only the happy hours"). Mam's Welshness and love of scholarship provided me with spiritual compass bearings but Dad's iconoclasm and anarchy satisfied other needs. Clennon was the private adventure, the Batman serial in which I played the cloaked crusader helped by Arthur's knights, horses, foxes, the GWR ratcatcher and the poacher, Tacker Willock. Along the frontiers of this Samuel Palmer landscape was the unbelievably exciting no-go area of heavy drinking.

Dad built his special Friday drunk on a foundation of farmhouse rough cider before switching to the more expensive and less potent draught bitter. He drank out of a sleever, topping up the pint with light fizzy stuff from a bottle marked Starkey, Knight and Ford Special Pale Ale. I guessed this was a sorcerer's brew concocted to dull the memory of a week's toil and to illumine the weekend. It turned the building site zombie into the public bar wit and prophet.

At about eight o'clock Dad came reeling home to collect Mam, ricochetting off the terrace walls, laughing and farting and running backwards for yards on his heels wearing a bemused Stan Laurel expression. The flies of his overalls were usually undone and his pockets bulged with loose change. Coins dribbled out when he sat down and his fireside armchair became my piggy bank till Mam saw me pocketing a handful of silver one evening and took over the business.

"I got filled-in by three blokes," he would begin. "They knocked me on the head and stole my money."

"Who were they, Dad?" I'd ask, although I knew the answer.

"Starkey, Knight and Ford," came the reply, and he would hoot with laughter and stumble around the kitchen while Mam tried to show him the incinerated remains of his roast meal in an effort to prick his conscience. But he was always too far gone to care about anything except pouring more beer into his face.

Why Mam ever bothered to cook for him on Fridays continues to puzzle me unless she needed to build her nag on the ruined roast like he built his beer drunk on scrumpy. This was just the overture to the Friday night performance. While Mam bawled at him Dad shaved and put on a collar and tie and his suit. Then he took Mam back with him to the crowded bar and sought the mysterious Leglessness that was the Holy Grail of every weekend session. As the pub was over the road it was considered proper to leave me alone for a couple of hours provided I had enough Dawe's ciderapple fizz, and Smith's crisps with the little blue bag of salt in the packet. Double summertime gave us long dusks which persisted through late August, smoking old gold around the backyards where the cockerels strutted and hens scratched the baked mud for kitchen scraps. The nine terrace houses were tiny smallholdings and in hot weather the whole neighbourhood reeked like a farmyard. Our rabbits scuffed the woodshavings and straw in the hutches by the dustbin opposite a patch of earth no bigger than a tablecloth which provided us with runner beans, lettuces and tomatoes. On the tin roof Dad's pigeons crooned, plump and relaxed and half-asleep yet tantalizingly out of reach of the cats. These lean, hard-boiled toms and promiscuous shes kept a very low profile until feeding time when they became daft and lovable for five minutes.

It was good to slip into this comfortable, Chaucerian world at dimpsey. Devonians hardly ever referred to day's end as dusk. It was dimpsey or dimsey – the soft fade away or dimming of light. The word has the texture of that drowsy interlude when animals and birds settle close to sleep and the countryside blooms magical. And I particularly loved the cool dimpseys which marked the end of summer and burgeoned to their full beauty in October.

My parents' simple, Friday night joy was contagious and swept me to the back gate and on into the narrow, deep alley. I stepped warily but he was there, Horseshit O'Flaherty, the most famous primary school kid in Paignton. He was an evacuee who had been abandoned by his London family to be brought up by a loving, over-indulgent elderly couple. Thinking adults called him the "effing cockney monster", and Horseshit claimed old Sid Collins, the catmeat man, had biffed a chopper at him for putting pepper in his horse's nosebag.

Dusk was O'Flaherty's kingdom. Then he would rise like Dracula out of his daydreaming to commit atrocities of astonishing originality, such as cremating live butterflies with a petrol lighter or blowing down the straw he had wedged in the frog's butt, or – and this led to his expulsion from Sunday School – the pressing of a live bee between the pages of a heavy Bible. Caligula's crimes paled beside his sadism but he was also the bravest boy I ever knew, possibly because he had less imagination than a building brick.

The unsavoury nickname was bestowed on him after an act of bravado unparalleled in juvenile folk history. Beryl Eccles dared Johnny O'Flaherty to eat one of the steaming conkers left behind by the white mare that pulled the Co-op coal cart. Three huge bites and it was gone, and Johnny wasn't even sick. He just stood there smiling and smacking his lips while I doubled-up and retched and Colin Yeo's face became a lighter shade of yellow. After such an amazing feat Horseshit O'Flaherty's immortality was guaranteed. I hated him but found it politic to pretend otherwise and keep him sweet. He was a gull-eyed, hatchet-faced, ginger-headed ten-year-old psychopath who was easily upset. Impetigo had done nasty things to his complexion.

"Ants' nest," he murmured, sucking back the spittle of concentration and nodding at the big, loaf-shaped cobbles. Black specks were kicking furiously in an expanding puddle of petrol.

"Watch," Horseshit commanded from the centre of a vast grin. He put a match to the pool and the flames danced round our knees, and then the cobbles were covered with pinheads of charcoal.

"Howja make a cat bark?" said Horseshit, lifting one of the charred corpses on a matchstick.

Ice churned in my stomach and I shook my head.

"Soak 'im in petrol, bung him on the fire and he goes woof!"

He flung up his arms, ecstatic, but my laughter rang very phoney and hollow.

"Anyway," Horseshit said, laying a cold little hand like a dead mouse on my arm, "where you goin', Carter the Farter?"

"Up my Gran's," I lied.

"What for – Farter?"

"She's ill."

"My gran's a miserable old turd," said Horseshit and he let

me go, thinking maybe that all grans were miserable old turds
and to visit them was a penance.

But Clennon Valley lay beyond O'Flaherty's knowing and
Friday night was the last railway station on the line to starry
infinity. Dusk called me to the watermeadows and orchards of
cider apples. Behind the breeze was the bleak smell of the sea. A
steam train puffed and clanked out of Goodrington goods yard,
moving slowly towards Kingswear under its own white cloud.
The bottom of the sky glowed like the belly of a mackerel, only
very soft and insubstantial. Gangs of herring gulls emerged from
it, sending their cries down long reaches of silence, yodelling to
each other and exchanging high-pitched hiccuping screams.

Dew-fall liberated scents which the green stuff in the allotments refused to release until the sun had set. Blackberries
glistened on the brambles and the elder corymbs were turning
purple amongst the rust of hedgerow haws. Trotting up Tanner's
Lane I caught a whiff of the cattle which had gone before me,
leaving their warm, damp body odour sandwiched between the
banks of red earth and the dark foliage of elm brush. Now I was
the fox whose stink clung to the elder stabs, whose passing had
left ginger whisps of fur snagged on the briars by the allotments.
Long-eared bats flickered through two fathoms of gloom, cutting under the leaves and skimming the rutted mud of the lane.
O lovely little winged mice who slumbered all winter in God's
cavernous nostrils! The darkening countryside was alive with
them and the swallows making one last sweep down the insect
trails before going to roost. And then the ghost moths dancing
and the mist stretched thin and white, wreathing the valley
osiers.

Friesians flashed me sidelong glances and dropped their
heads again to crop the hush. My sandals were soaked and each
squelchy step set the bullocks' ears twitching and the yarrow
and ragwort rocking. I left behind me a line of small black holes
and the sweet, mouldy reek of ooze. The grass and nettles were
unpleasant to wade through. Spiders' webs, surprisingly wet and
heavy, clung to my naked flesh but I was careful not to harm the
spiders who decided to sprint up my trouser legs to find sanctuary in my underpants. O'Flaherty would have dismembered
them, the tip of his tongue protruding and the tell-tale drool
depending from his lower lip. Flies, spiders, moths and grass-
hoppers had all received the O'Flaherty treatment. I shuddered

and removed the daddy-long-legs from the nettle-blisters on my right calf. God would get the cockney monster in the end. Hadn't he punished the Japs by letting the Americans drop atom bombs on their cities? The Japs were cruel little buggers like O'Flaherty. But the bombs sorted them out, Dad crowed. Well, maybe God had even worse plans for Horseshit. Maybe the spirit spiders would pull off his legs. God got you in the end. He always won, and yet, I thought, pushing through the final clump of reeds to the edge of the stream, how boring it must be to know everything that is happening and is going to happen everywhere. You could plan your picnics a million years in advance. But if God knew they would drop the atom bomb why let the war start in the first place? "Don't speak to me about God," Mam sobbed, hiding the front page photographs of Belsen. "If there's a God he's bloody cruel and living's just a horrible joke. Thousands of little kids! What's one bloody crucifixion compared with that!"

And why was Bertie Slater's left leg withered and shorter than his right? And why did the all-merciful, all-loving Almighty arrange for sparrow chicks to drop out of the nest into Nibs's greedy gob? I sat with my face close to the water beside the stream. A moorhen said "prook-prook" from the flags and sedges. Quiet silver reaches had escaped the current and here the water-fiddlers preyed on minute insects and larvae, hunting in packs and swarming around unlucky bluebottles to siphon off the juices. All sorts of ghoulish things were going on under the surface. Great water-beetles like aliens from another planet were slaughtering and devouring tiny fish, and the hideously masked dragonfly larva was also busy at the murder game down among the bubbles of marsh gas. Lots of dead flies traced the thickly silent flow of the water, torpedoing the bubble sculptures. They were brilliant green, and gold and purple gleamed on thorax and body. Occasionally one of them vanished and a grotesque dimpled the surface before sinking into darkness with its victim held in a cold embrace.

But the stars glittering on the film of light which separated that aquatic nightmare from my world of cattle, mist and hawking bats remained just as remote and indifferent. Human pain or joy never lofted to those places, and the death of a star was of no consequence because it touched no human heart. The sea breeze curled the flags at the tips, cast the dandelion fairies adrift and sent the white breast feathers of gulls and barn owls floating up the valley. Daws came to the stream to swim and drink. To see a bird actually swimming, using its wings like a pair of arms, did not seem incredible. I accepted everything nature offered without question because I lived in it.

The mist spread and thickened, sitting on the watermeadows in horizontal bands. Cows lay close together patiently waiting for sleep, and a heron whispered up from the drainage gut looking huge and clumsy. Bright beads of moisture encrusted the grasses and reeds and hung from the leaves of the sow thistles. Above the mist, hills clustered on three horizons and over the dump and railway embankment to the east was the sea. Tiny fields bounded by hedges of thorn, hazel, elm and ash patterned the hillsides and no buildings were visible except a couple of linhays. From the earliest possible age I was told that I was rooted in this. I had the blood.

"The trees are sacred," Grandad said. "They cast their shadows to worship God."

"All the trees?" I asked.

"Every one. And they sing for joy. It says so in the Bible."

Gran bunched elder leaves in a vase to keep the flies out of her living room.

"The trees provide fruit and shade, and wood for the home and the fire," Grandad said.

I remember him lifting me into a giant oak whose branches shot out like the points of a stag's head.

"It hasn't changed much since I was a boy," Grandad continued. "And I daresay it'll be the same when your children are born."

But he was wrong. The war reprieved the paradise of shire horses, owls and herons but its days were numbered. It was not pretty enough and there was nothing to entice the manufacturers of country calendars or the tourist. Mercifully I was ignorant of its fate as I hacked and roared and skulked through the last years of the 1940s. Boyhood itself was an intense adventure with no foreseeable end. The visions bloomed and were leading me to the end of the rainbow, not in search of the proverbial crock of gold but to find the perfect Devon trout stream fringed with flawless alders and rowans under the perfect sky of spring. Here I would swim and bask in the sun and hug the trees and bite the vivid green leaves. I was the red indian, never the cowboy, living the animal life against the slow shift of the seasons. And Clennon Valley was the first great vision, one of God's better sonnets, so utterly English it was almost a rural cliché. Happiness swelled my heart whenever I put the allotments behind me and lifted my eyes to the small, rounded hills. The seasons played on my consciousness, drawing me into the brotherhood we share with living creatures and wild things.

I loved the smell of the farmyards and smallholdings whose breath ascended from medieval Britain bearing the reek of piggeries, chicken runs and middens. The soil was cared for and gave good yields. Corn, grass and roots were eaten by the animals, recycled and returned to enrich the land. Men farmed according to laws older than Stonehenge but today the bond has been broken and England is covered with animal factories. To stand under the drooping boughs of the cider apple trees hooded with the scent of ripe fruit was heaven, and to walk through a green and silver sea of grass at dawn was to shed my human shape and become the fox. But best of all I knew that animals experienced joy in fellowship. Bathsheba, the old shire mare of Cider Mill Farm, would gallop to greet Solomon when he was led into the field after work. Then they would run together, fluting soft love talk through their noses to roll in the grass with arching necks and manes spreading loose on the air.

Now, again, I was in the good unspoilt place alone, crouching in one of twilight's blue hollows. A full and golden moon was rising out of Torbay, cutting a furrow across the meadow. What I absorbed then was not built of words. The shaping of it would come later as the need to write grew out of despair for the vanishing splendour. How long the summer of my ninth year seemed but that Friday dusk beside the stream has never faded. I find echoes of it in Wordsworth's poetry and in all the great verse whose beauty has been harvested from the human spirit and the open air.

Always at dimpsey the white owls eclipsed the dog star to quarter the rat runs of the rubbish dump. Down-fringed wings carried them silently across the drainage canal to the mounds of garbage where they loitered with murderous intent; you could set your watch by them. They had hunted even during the air raids, with the bombs crumping and the searchlights flashing from shore batteries and observation posts all round Torbay. Mr Hannaford, the cowman of Litstone Farm, called them "owulls" and showed me their nest in the linhay. But Mr Hannaford was dead, along with young George Parsons of Hookhill. They were lying in the same ship at the bottom of the North Atlantic. To die so far from home was the saddest fate.

My skin prickled as the owls cruised overhead, noiselessly like mercury poured onto blue velvet. They were well-mated and joyful in the eternal Now of their lives. And so were the rabbits hopping out of the hedgerow warrens to feed, and the cock pheasant flinging a final challenge at the world from the brackened steeps. Light ebbed and the hills crowded in. Sleep had come quickly to the waterfowl and songbirds, and the buzzards of Clennon Wood had sealed their eyes to the sky.

I got up and stretched and saw the fox leave his kennel of reeds to scatter the fleas from his belly with a stiff hind foot. The slow swallowing of trees, hedges and fields by darkness had begun but the fox seemed drugged by the beauty around him. He stood up on his hind legs and started to dance, head thrown back and jaws snapping in ecstasy. Round and round he twirled, stumbling sometimes and vanishing only to bob up again, waggling his pointed muzzle at the stars and showing me his grin. And I knew he was more than a wild creature. He was one of the animal gods who had escaped from the Mabinogion to drink the starlight, maybe to attain a sort of spiritual legless-ness.

The fox-god danced on with waving front feet and the clack of jaws. He arched out of the reeds and fell back to pirouette and shake his head and repeat the movements. Then I think he read my presence on the breeze and stared briefly at me before loping away. Madog, the Welsh called him. Madog the dancing fox, his fur sparking moonlight while he did his occult thing in the mist.

Many years later the mystery was stripped from the incident. I was on Dartmoor close to some ponds when a fox trotted into the meadow and danced for me. But it was a very practical dance for he was jumping about on his hindlegs catching and eating the craneflies which were hatching out of the leather-jackets amongst the grasses. Luckily science kept its distance in the Forties and nothing mundane clouded my imagination to ruin the pageant.

*   *   *

Turning for home I saw the stars bright and enormous behind

Cider Mill Hill and heard the zither and chirr of crickets along the hedges. It was cold in my grey flannel shirt and khaki shorts so I ran to get warm. Lights gleamed from the windows of the big houses along Dartmouth Road and my shadow glided before me under gas lamps that wheezed and chuckled. Breathlessly I unlocked the back door and crept into the dark little kitchen and turned the lampwick right up as soon as it was lit. Nibs brushed against my legs and I had to pick her up and kiss her head to make her stop. Then I wolfed a heap of pickles and cheese and thick slices of silvery-pink ham. Everything on the kitchen table smelt of the sea or the countryside. Rabbits in fur, chickens or ducks in feather, mackerel, bloaters and kippers hummed with odours modern noses would find offensive. Nature was constantly spilling into our lives to hone the pastoral instinct and make us aware of our position in the cosmos. Rationing helped. People had to look to the woods and fields and sea for meat, and I never tired of rabbit pie or a fry-up of young mackerel – always referred to as 'joeys' by Devonians. The supermarkets belonged to a future bent on divorce from our rural heritage, a future full of things neatly packaged and hermetically sealed and tasteless.

Rationing forced us to set snares and poach and take the odd fowl from somebody's hen house, but killing to live in many cases led to a reverence for life. Certainly there was little of the squeamishness which is saluted today and confused with genuine sympathy for animals. How odd to hear fox hunting condemned over escalope of veal by women wearing cosmetics which have been tested on living laboratory rabbits. My father's generation were more caring human beings than my generation and I'm sure this had something to do with their closeness to the earth. They felt their way through the seasons and drew strength from elementals we scorn. Working the land meant giving as well as taking, but 'where your heart is, there is your treasure also'. It was written on the sampler in Gran's hall.

A little of the pastoral glory that lit South Devon in Dad's days honeycombed my childhood and there was no reason to suspect it would ever fade. But we have been betrayed by spiritual bankruptcy and the soil cries out for the gnarled, loving hands which long ago were folded over hearts stilled by old age.

2
Commando Raids

We had never had a family holiday but that was OK because few
of our neighbours went away except to funerals or weddings.
The working class who lived by the seaside were the happy
captives of their circumstances and prejudices. We weren't poor
and we weren't comfortably off, and Dad was an unambitious
carpenter and could not save a penny. The only way we might
have managed a few days out of the rut was by returning the
empties to the off-sales. But Mam's pride prevented her from
staggering to the pub's side-door with a couple of frails full of
half-pint Mackeson and Guinness bottles. Dad had to pop them
over the counter at the rate of one a visit in case people got the
impression we were hard-up.

So the mountain of empties grew in the shed and no one
thought of turning it into a charabanc trip to the Lakes or a day
trip to London. For months the yard smelt like a brewery and I
often found mice on their backs, legs pointed at the sky, over-
come by the fumes. In emergencies, though, the "bottle bank"
was as useful as today's credit card. Six pint Guinness empties
paid for my Saturday morning cinema or two American comics
or half a guinea pig; but before I could really milk the business
Dad sold the lot for half-price to the coalman.

My father's Homeric booze-ups elevated him to the working

class peerage. Landlords beamed when he swaggered through the public bars, his wages burning a hole in his pocket and his tongue hanging out. He was a spit-and-sawdust cavalier, the chip shop Valentino cutting his way through the tobacco fug with flashing quips like Errol Flynn. Even the Co-op off-the-peg, double-breasted grey suit failed to blunt his charisma. When drunk he was generous and good-humoured, full of carbon dioxide and mischief. I loved to see him come rolling in after chucking-out time, a flagon of light ale in one hand, his free arm round Mam's waist, the pair of them ruddy-faced and twinkling like crab-apples.

Fridays and Saturdays refused to die. They dragged and on and on and I was rarely in bed before midnight. These were Dad's Two-Pot nights, and I would hear him roll out of bed and scuff about in the dark for the chamber pot. By dawn a brace of them would almost be full. I always knew when the evening's beer was frothing up to his thumb for the loud hiss settled into a dull, melodious purr followed by a short pause, a sigh and the gentle thud of the vessel being replaced under the bed. And every so often his rear end would impersonate a euphonium or warble a trombone solo.

Lying awake I would cry with laughter and watch the white rectangles of moonlight blaze and dissolve on the wall as clouds swept across the sky.

* * *

That morning Mr Gowman's pullet cockerel was crowing early and the other macho birds started returning the hard talk with interest. Soon scores of cocks were heralding the dawn all over Paignton. In six of the terrace backyards the fowls were excavating for earthworms that had miraculously survived the talons and beaks by burrowing deep and resisting the temptation to wriggle to the surface whenever a hen tapped the mud with a foot, imitating the patter of raindrops. Horseshit O'Flaherty had grabbed Mr Gowman's prize bantam in a daring raid on VE night while the randy old devil was up in his bedroom, telescope trained on the convent school windows, praying for a glimpse of big girlies getting ready for sleep. Alas, the nuns were wise to the weakness of the flesh and the curtains were pulled at dusk.

But cockcrow reached through my being to emotions which remained mysterious for years. Even then I had a highly developed sense of history and due to the splendid spiritual chaos at the centre of my parents' lives, was never the prisoner of Time.

I got up and went out into the pale morning to scrump fruit. At the bottom of Elmsleigh Road was a plum tree bowing under its load of fat victorias. The posh people from the big house with the inside lavatory let the fruit rot on the boughs. The luscious purple plums would crack and bleed juice. Fastened like lovers to these oozings the wasps clung ferociously and had to be flicked off before I could stuff the plunder in my shirtfront.

Dawn was the best time for scrumping and poaching. The local beat bobby – PC Leonard Budworth – took himself and his job very seriously but had decided all criminals were crepuscular. According to him the spivs and cosh boys and common-or-garden thieves belonged to a vast army of drones whose bums had to be dynamited off the mattress if you wanted them up at a reasonable hour. Thus on Budworth's patch lead was removed from church roofs at dawn, poaching reached its peak at dawn and I came tippy-toe at dawn to the plum tree.

But the victorias weren't the sole reason for my commando raids. It was good to be the only human alive in the world, answering the cockcrows from my blood, forgetting words and word-crochet under the bubbling chatter of the starlings. The choir of diamond-eyed birds scattered over the rooftops, full of life's brightness, and I lay on the sandstone wall letting the keen fresh juice squirt against the back of my throat in a fine spray. Tom cats flattened themselves to the tops of walls as I did and among the snail shells were the small bones and beaks of slaughtered birds.

Before the lights came on in Skinner's Dairy I trotted up the lane to the garden of the retired bank manager's house. Old Man Forsey and I had been enemies ever since his wife had caught me scooping goldfish from their ornamental pond. He marked me as a member of the great army of unwashed have-nots that had pulled down Churchill and installed Attlee and a labour government. His mindless arrogance and snobbery have their echoes throughout history and were celebrated every Empire Day. Hundreds of thousands of working class children really believed in that "Land of Hope and Glory" which dads and uncles and elder brothers had shed blood for. Yet to men like Forsey a carpenter or a plumber or a brickie was inferior, representing as he did the Bolshie threat to the status quo. And this middle class contempt was absorbed into the collective consciousness of my class and distilled into an enduring hatred of social injustice.

A rapport between the lower class and the upper class did exist (on upper class terms) when I was a boy, and the middle class provided a grey no-man's-land of respectability where eccentrics wandered at their peril. Dad hardly ever had a bad word for the "toff" despite his unashamedly idle existence. And if Lord Fozzlepot was a drunkard, a gambler and a womanizer he grew in Dad's estimation. He never pretended drudgery was a dignified state and he was greedy for leisure and individual freedom.

"I'd crawl a hundred miles over broken glass with Lord Lovat", he'd say. "But I wouldn't share a fart with your average Church of England vicar or that prat Forsey."

Mrs Forsey had locked me up in the coal shed after the goldfish incident while her husband called the police. Dad thought this was unsporting and let Forsey know it one day outside the Home & Colonial.

"Don't be impertinent, Carter," Forsey drawled, turning his back on Dad and dismissing him like a servant.

If Mam and Granny Carter had not clung to Dad's arms while the veins stood out on his white, taut face he would have committed GBH. Yet his loathing of jingoistic frolics was born of insight more than prejudice. He saw beyond the Union Jack waving to the blood and misery and pathos of it all.

"There wasn't a lot of flag waving on the Somme," he said. "And the Jarrow Marchers didn't sing Rule Britannia."

Standing in the playground of Jubilee Street girls' school on Empire Day I found myself gripped by the tide of patriotism. We sang the great national songs and listened to council officials making speeches. The older children knew what it was all about. England was the centre of a huge empire and we were part of a magnificent nation. God save King George VI. Salute the flag. Jesus Christ! – how I loved King and Country but mostly the country which to me was Clennon Valley.

Despite his cynicism Dad was intensely patriotic and romantic. He perpetuated the myth of upper-lower class detente, recalling how those sad ex-public schoolboys led bayonet charges in Flanders armed with nothing but swagger sticks, stiff upper lips and guts. Courage, you see, was the common ground which the under-nourished and the over-fed trod together and Death provided the equality that democracy could never quite pull off.

The walls around the Forsey stronghold were high and hackled with broken glass cemented upright into sandstone. Barbed wire had been tacked along the top of the gates. So I climbed the pear tree in the neighbouring garden and swung down onto Forsey's compost heap like a micro-chip Johnny Weissmuller. Then I picked a bunch of chrysanths for Mam before doing the deed.

I had just enough strength to drag the stone pixie to the apple tree in the centre of the lawn. Up he went to grin puckishly from his roost. And from the hook of his little fishing line I hung one of Dad's old working socks. The performance was rounded off by ringing the kitchen doorbell until the Forsey household lurched irritably out of sleep. The sudden flash of light at the top of the stairs sent me racing up Grosvenor Road and into the alley, cockadoodling with triumph and glowing with wickedness.

By now the blurred gold of the new days was touching the highest leaves of the chestnuts at the bottom of our terrace. I stopped and peered through the cracks of every gate I passed, anxious for a glimpse of the fowls Mam would never permit Dad to keep in our backyard. In ramshackle prisons of chicken wire the gaudy cockerels strutted and bragged, fixing me with manic, red-rimmed eyes and lifting their legs to execute a ridiculous slow-motion goose-step of sexuality which the biddies ignored.

"Cockaroodle-oo" went Reggie, the Merediths' big Rhode Island Red rooster, and his yellow hooks made token gestures in the mud that held nothing but the reek of hen mutes.

Bronze, purple, moss green, turquoise, gold, scarlet and sienna feathers caught the first gleams of morning as the rainbow samurai paraded under larder windows, and their harems clucked and laid eggs. Me and Doodlebug, the Merediths' terrible black and tan tom, ran poulterer's eyes over them. Warm, succulent flesh fuelled our day dreams but chicken was central to Christmas – that splendid point in time where excitement whirpooled, dragging me down into gluttony and sensual bliss.

The yellowing of leaves and the sight of fowls decorating the margins of a September morning brought Christmas to mind. Soon I would be counting the weeks, then the days and hours to Christmas Eve. The robin singing his autumn song from Miss Millman's clothes line triggered off the process, but first the harvest had to be brought home.

*   *   *

Three shire horses were stabled at Cider Mill Farm: Solomon, Bathsheba and Edward. Butch Meredith and I could earn a few shillings in the summer holidays pulling ragwort and singling turnips for Farmer Bickford. But we would have worked for just the privilege of riding the magnificent animals to and from the fields. Their passing some years later broke my heart and whenever I visit the valley and look up at Cider Mill Hill the pain rises on recollection, keen and sharp. The shadow of lovely times lost forever falls across my life while rural England continues to decay and vanish. Already much of the prose and poetry I wrote to celebrate a particular corner of Devon has become a requiem.

Cider Mill Farm stood in the coombe a hundred yards back from Dartmouth Road at Waterside, sheltered from the easterly winds by a hill and jostled on three sides by orchards of bramleys and cider apples. The tall, gabled house of grey stone was reached by a flight of steps from the farmyard where the outbuildings collected moss and ivy and really looked as if they had risen from the soil with the trees. Border collies and old wellingtons usually littered the farmhouse porch but we couldn't wait to get to the stable.

It was a place of great dark beams, whitewashed walls, whispering straw and shadows full of the trappings of Arthurian chivalry; chains, bits, halters, collars, brasses hung from hooks, and the beautiful brown gloom smelt heavily of soiled bedding. Mr Bickford had flu so we were met by the horseman-cum-carter, a Geordie named Ernie Brooks. Not everyone who looks after animals is enobled by daily contact with innocent creatures but Ernie possessed qualities Adam left behind in Eden. He was a squat, long-armed, bespectacled character whose fierce exterior concealed a rare gentleness. He crooned to the shires, breathing endearments through pursed lips, his potato-nosed ugliness mellowed by the glow of the hurricane lamp.

We helped him water the horses and watching them drink he would tell us as he had done many times before that the shire was the largest horse in the world. And they would stamp hooves the size of dinner plates and snuffle from velvety noses as though his voice pleased them. Their eyes were large and slumberous, tranquil and brown like the eyes of cattle. They turned their heads to watch us combing the tufts on their lower legs. These hanks of hair were called feathers and had to be kept clean or the animals' feet became diseased. The light grooming continued while they ate a breakfast of oats and hay, and Ernie prepared their midday nosebags of chaffed straw and oats. Finally we led the shires out into the yard where Edward was hitched to the wagon. Then came the magic prelude when Butch and I rode Solomon and Bathsheba up the gleaming stony lane to the meadow and put them out to grass before running on to the wheatfield to earn our half-crowns.

Fragments of morning dovetailed to become a Pre-Raphaelite dream. Sunlight glossed the jackdaw's head and twinkled on beaks and berries. But the light in the rabbits' eyes came from within and had its origins somewhere beyond birth.

The bottoms of the hedges were patched here and there with the webs of garden spiders, and among the reddening bramble leaves yellow toadflax thrust from dark, vole-haunted grottoes of moss and hartstongue ferns. Hen chaffinches were rocking the stands of hogweed in a noisy flock and for a moment they filled the lane, flitting ahead of us, fanning out and coming together, until telepathy sucked them over the hazels as one to vanish like a shower of rain.

Butch and I took turns to pitch sheaves onto the wagon and lead the horse. The casual labourer, a morose Devonian called Tony, was laying the straw foundation for the rick. A fortnight previously the harvest machine had cut and pumped out sheaves which we had stood upright, six to a stook so that the rain ran off them and the wind passed through them drying and airing the ears and stalks. "Stooked wheat must hear the churchbells ring twice before tis ready for carting" was an old country saying. Higher and higher grew the wagon load of sheaves and my hands were singing from gripping thistles and nettles. The ghosts of poppies, scabious, knapweed and cornflowers flew briefly through the air from the prongs of the pitchfork, bound-up with the wheat. And I was riding summer's rustling cortège.

The wagon bumped and juddered up the field, its cargo

swaying and threatening to tip over at every jolt. Throughout the day the shadows of the remaining stooks lengthened and the stack grew under Tony's expert hands and feet. The rhythm was broken only by his need to ease the irritation of his haemorrhoids, fingers buried in the seat of his trousers.

"Piles," he explained, catching my eye – "the grapes of wrath."

"Tony was a pilot in the war," Ernie said during the afternoon tea break.

I frowned up at him, trying to hide my disbelief. The idea of Tony flying a spitfire was as unacceptable as the notion of my Dad addressing the AGM of the Temperance Society.

"Tis true," Tony said. "I was a pilot right yer on the varm."

"Lyin' bugger," Butch said under his breath.

"Ernie would muck-out the 'orses," Tony continued solemnly, "and I'd pilit here and pilit there and pilit everybloodywhere."

Butch and I grinned. It was our sort of humour – basic, primary school wit. Then Tony told two long dirty jokes which we didn't understand and found embarrassing despite our earthy upbringing. But Ernie smiled and turned the conversation to farmwork and horses. A grey cloud of woodpigeons settled out of gun-shot on the field. Leaves danced down from the scrub elms behind the stack and the sun shone from an open sky above the valley and the burnished shoulder of stubble.

The field was small and by late evening the rick was being thatched and we were free to become Knights of the Round Table. Butch wasn't much of a horseman so he let me ride Solomon and settled for the less frisky old age pensioner Bathsheba. At dimpsey the sweetness of life filtered through every fibre of my body but the joy was tinged with sadness and it was a funny feeling like smiling through tears.

Old warm leathery smell of horse; scent of leaf-mould and mud and the sea; ducks flopping onto Pucksbog; the whirr and hiccup of pheasants; and the sound of the stream rising as the hush grew. Out of harness the shires snapped playfully at each other, speaking their own dawn-of-creation language. Ernie had the feel of it if not the sense of it. Like my father he did not think hard work was a religion but his dealings with horses were really continuous love affairs sublimated by trust and loyalty that never faltered.

Harvest was a good time. I never saw the horses covered in white lather as they were after ploughing the heavy wet soil. Their happiness was the echo of my own emotions. Back to the stables we came, Lludd and Llefelys, Mabinogion heroes mounted on their warhorses. Mrs Bickford brought over our pay and Ernie said we were good boys and the shires were watered, fed, washed and brushed. Outside on the hill the summer had been laid to rest and turned into a castle. Already the first rats would be arriving to join the mice and other small creatures taking up their tenancy of the rick. Walking home across the darkening farmland I saw Vega mirrored in a cow's eye and heard the barn owls calling. The sudden bursts of white from the night mist were the scuts of departing rabbits.

"You got a barnie's egg?" Butch asked.

"Two," I said.

"Swop one for an oystercatcher's?"

"Oystercatcher's and a kingfishers's."

"Sod off! I only got two kingfisher's."

I knew this and nodded. His kingfisher eggs were the envy of every boy in the neighbourhood and I had lusted after the Meredith treasure for nearly a year.

"Barn owl and shag," I said slyly, trading on his weakness for seabirds' eggs which vertigo rendered a frustrating vice.

"Barn owl, shag *and* razorbill."

"OK," I said and we spat on our palms and shook hands to seal the bargain.

*　　*　　*

Gaslight bloomed and the back-street world was handed over to the children. We filled it with laughter, shouts and screams. Dark little shapes flew along the pavements, skidding on the wet beech leaves in front of the Marist Convent or gathering on street corners to chat or play conkers or organize mischief. The fine evenings belonged to us and we breathed life into dusks made mistier by the smoke from chimneys and bonfires.

"The police called," Mam said, banging my meal down on the table so that the potatoes jumped up off the plate and back again, splashing me with gravy. She glared at me and caught me behind the ear with her knuckles. The smack of those bony fingers made my eyes water but didn't wipe the grin off my face.

"Police?" I said innocently.

This time she rapped my head with the handle of the bread knife.

"Don't give me any of your lip. It was about Mr Forsey's pixie. Dozens of times he's had to take it out of the apple tree. And you've been swipin' stuff from his garden. The chrysanths are in the bin, by the way."

"He saw me, did he Mam?"

"He says he saw a boy like you and there's not another little bugger like you running wild around here."

"Did the police say it was me?"

"No – but they warned you to stop being bloody smart. Next time it'll be a summons. And then what would the neighbours think?"

"I don't like Budworth."

The bread knife handle went spock! on my skull.

"Budworth didn't come," Mam said. "They sent Sergeant Nathan and he spoke about Reform School."

The liver was crisp and dark brown, the bacon curled at the tips; the gravy was rich and the boiled potatoes and the peas did not dissolve on the tongue. But the golden brown rings of fried onion, married to the other vegetables and the meat, produced the Hallelujah Chorus from my taste buds. We rarely ate dessert and never started a meal with soup. Mam's dinners, with everything piled high on the plate, were always more than enough, and supper from the pickle jars rang the perfect angelus in my soul.

Throughout the meal I heard the kettles singing on the gas stove and the bubble and rattle of the saucepans full of boiling water. Saturday night was bath night and I stood in the zinc tub before the fire while Mam soaped me and rinsed me so many times I had a pink phosphorescent glow. Then as she applied the big rough towel and held me close she would croodle Suo Gan, the loveliest of Welsh lullabies.

Sitting on the threadbare rug, my head brushed and shining like gold in the firelight, I could smile away her anxieties. But beneath the charm I was trying to decide whether or not I'd get up early and tree the Forsey pixie again. They would not be expecting another commando raid immediately after the police visit. Or maybe I'd parcel-up a dead rat and leave it on their doorstep. Then Mrs Forsey would snarl at me when we met in the newsagents at the top of the terrace. And I would switch on my Borgia grin and step on her grand-daughter's toes.

"Bloody little guttersnipe," Old Man Forsey had roared into the darkness one memorable night. His wife had tipped the dead crow out of her coal scuttle and delivered the most unearthly shriek as it flopped onto the fire. From the roof of the Forsey garage we followed the action, hankies stuffed in our mouths, shaking with silent laughter. Me and Butch and Colin Yeo marvelled at Mrs Forsey's prolonged hysterics and the stupidity of their fat spaniel who should have sniffed us out but was obsessed with his own private parts which he was constantly licking.

The wind moaned in the chimney, rising to a boom then fading only to return and make the fire puff smoke into the room. The clock chipped away at my boyhood and whittled the precious days I spent so carelessly. Evening lifted from the pages of the *Rupert Annual* and occupied my knowing. The window shook and everything inside our warm back room was suddenly orchestrated to create cosiness and contentment. I could hear the gurgle of Mam's gastric juices and her breathing and an occasional sigh. Then tea would be poured and sugar whispered through the steaming surface until silence settled and the clock gained control. Whenever Nibs pushed open the door to come in, the flames leapt up and gold and scarlet puddled the ceiling.

Mam and Dad were still over the pub when I climbed the stairs by candlelight and pushed the hot water bottle to the bottom of the bed with my feet. The cool nights had silenced the cricket that had sung so bravely through late summer. A haystack of sleep rolled onto me and smothered me but I woke once to find the room full of moonlight.

3
Dust and Ashes

I hated Sundays, those prayer-soaked, funereal glumdays. But unlike the other children I didn't have the spectre of Monday morning and school hanging over me. The bombing in Bristol where we had lived for a brief spell during the war had shattered my nerves and I suffered from a variety of nervous complaints including St Vitus' Dance and a mysterious condition the doctor called Night Terror. I'd leap out of some awful dream, usually choking and screaming to find Mam hugging me, bringing me back into myself. They said it was shell-shock but I'm convinced the trauma could be traced back to the bronchial-pneumonia I endured as an infant. On many occasions I nearly drowned in my own mucus and I recall the doctor clearing my trachea with a crude, scooplike instrument. Whatever it was chased me through sleep to resurrect the terror I had buried in my subconscious.

Apparently rest and fresh air cured most mental illnesses so I was kept home from school for months on end and encouraged to run wild. Left to my own devices it seemed logical I should develop the savage's vision of life and nature. Fortunately Mam taught me to read and write before I was five and I was already picking up and decoding the minutiae of the seasons on the radar screen of my spirit. And the poetry she had learnt by heart at school and recited aloud, simple stuff like Wordsworth's 'Daffodils' and 'Lucy Gray', had a profound effect. The unbearable beauty of words made music has pursued me ever since. Later, in my teens, whenever I imagined God was speaking to me through the wilderness places he used the language of Wordsworth. On these solitary boyhood expeditions to Clennon I understood

> The silence that is in the starry sky,
> The sleep that is among the lonely hills.

* * *

The Salvation Army brass band marched down St Michael's Road past Evans' chip shop, pom-pommed round the corner and up the little bit of hill to Elmsleigh Road and on down over the railway crossing to the seafront. The houses were very still and the streets empty but Mam's chatter ruffled the sabbath hush. Clennon Valley smelt of woodsmoke and tired trees. A flock of longtailed tits exploded from the hedgerow thorns and Mam and I crept along the brow of the sheep pasture gathering the mushrooms and dropping them into the basket. She wore old wellingtons and a green headscarf. The October sun lit the blond tresses stirring on her forehead; and to me she was the loveliest creature God had ever made. Golden brown countryside rolled around us. A buzzard skirled; a green woodpecker undulated away like a little kite being pulled behind a running child; rooks cawed from the stubble.

"That's pretty," Mam said, and I followed her gaze.

Blue mist filled the lap of the valley and from it rose a heron, climbing through the sunshine and swinging west towards the Dart.

"I love the autumn," she continued.

Under the hedge a crow jauntily walked up the carcass of a sheep to get at the eyes.

"I like crows," I said, knowing the remark would be unpopular.

"Crows peck out lambs' eyes, Bri."

"Why did God make 'em then, Mam?"

"Maybe he don't care about animals. There's lots of things he don't care about – like the little children who got killed when that German plane hit the church in Torquay."

"I shot a bluetit with my catapult last Wednesday."

"Why? Bluetits are lovely little birds."

"I gave it to Tacker Willocks' ferret."

"You mustn't kill songbirds, Bri. We used to feed our ferrets on sparrows in feather and chickens' heads. Never bluetits. Sparrows eat grain and there's lots of them."

"Can I have an air pistol, Mam?"

"No you bloody can't. You're enough trouble as it is."

"I'll run away from home."

She grinned and said, "Good."

After the roast dinner which we ate around one o'clock Mam and Dad took me for a long walk. We went up Fisher Street, down Winner Street which was one of Paignton's oldest thoroughfares, climbed Colley End Road to Kings Ash and wandered out into the farmland. The lanes were deep, narrow and muddy. Buff- and brown-speckled oak leaves rustled down to swell the mush of yellow hazel and elm leaves in the red gruel. But we did not miss many of the filberts and at Blagdon Dad filled his pockets with walnuts.

The country road ran crookedly from Barton Pines to Totnes, passing high above the coombes and spinneys before dropping into the ancient hamlet of Berry Pomeroy. The vast panorama of South, West and Mid-Devon opened before us – a far-off glimpse of Dartmoor straight ahead and, to the left, hill upon rounded hill racing through the distant haze of the South Hams. One day I promised myself I'd walk to those dim horizons and discover what it was that saddened and excited me.

Sometimes Dad carried me on his shoulders whistling tunes like "Roll out the Barrel" and "Colonel Bogey", or singing snippets of gibberish:

"Articabs and choakajiz, ten barb roobi-a-stick" (Artichokes and cabbages, rhubarb ten bob a stick).

Then we headed for home up the main Totnes Road into dimpsey. From the hilltop we caught a glimpse of the sea and Berry Head lighthouse winking from the grey darkfall. And the churchbells rang out right across Devon, village and town taking up the music so that it filled every corner of Sunday.

Under the oxblood-coloured plough of Blagdon Hill the church of Collaton St Mary stood among tall trees, its windows glowing palely golden. Opposite the churchyard was a small meadow where the brook ran against the hedge. We stopped by the five-barred gate to feed the horses and Dad called to them, his voice thick with the affection that always flavoured his chats with animals. O the lovely Devon burr softening the Rs and the words turning on his tongue like earth behind the plough – heavy and rich.

The horses were suddenly there in the dimpsey, breathing the scent of crushed grass. Six dark shapes nuzzled each other and lifted their heads as if to drink the bell-music. Then they raced away to the shadows of the great, black elms. Those work animals found true liberty at dusk. They gazed from deep, mysterious dreams into fabled places where horses are kings. Turning to walk on I heard them thundering around the field and I heard them again yesterday when I re-read Dylan Thomas's 'Fern Hill'.

$$* \quad * \quad *$$

Tea was called supper on Sundays. There were usually cuts of cold meat off the joint, pickled beetroot and red cabbage, cheese, and potato cake washed down with rough cider – the genuine farmhouse scrumpy Dad got from Yalberton Lane. He worked his way steadily through two flagons and read Wilkie Collins or Conan Doyle in his armchair before the blaze of a fire that rapidly made an oven of the backroom. He loved Sherlock Holmes and Dickens' characters and Hardy's Wessex and Arnold Bennet's 'Five Towns'. If I could get his nose out of a book he would strum the mandolin he kept upstairs for special occasions. He played most tunes by ear but wasn't as good as his father whose mandolin band had performed twice a week at Deller's Cafe during the reign of Edward VII.

With Dad settling into his literature and his scrumpy Mam got out the tiddly winks and we sat at the table tiddling and winking and giggling every time Nibs pounced on one of the polished counters. The room was our starship of warmth cruising through the night. It was furnished haphazardly and had a comforting, lived-in feel. Only the lino was new. The rest of the bits and pieces – the table and three hard-backed chairs, two chintz armchairs, a little sidetable and the best sideboard the Co-op furniture department could provide – had been assembled hastily during the latter part of the war after four years of purgatory in furnished lodgings.

And contrary to Old Man Forsey's propaganda it wasn't a

hive of Bolshevik activity. Dad was a Churchill fan and had a framed *Picture Post* cover portrait of the war leader on the wall facing the fireplace. The cigar and victory salute were prominent – the salute which the plebs gleefully reversed as a rigid, two-fingers gesture of defiance and scorn.

Mam detested the great man and said he ought to have an apple in his big fat chops, not a cigar. But Dad championed the individual and spoke of vague, messianic figures, destiny and Britain as the centre of the universe. My Mother being a celt and a Morgan ran on the high octane fuel of primitive Christianity and labour party slogans. Her raw Old Testament religion was often eclipsed by atheism born of frustration and misery. Her politics were parochial, blinkered, painfully sincere, a cry from the heart for Jerusalem among the dark satanic mills. They sprang from living in cramped little houses with no bathroom and the lavatory up the yard.

"Men are expected to go down the mines," she said. "Or slog their guts out on building sites or farms or fishing boats, doing the heaviest, dirtiest jobs. But them who had the houses built decided we were some sort of dumb animals that didn't need bathrooms or three bedrooms or a decent bit of garden."

The drudgery reached into the sculleries of those two-up, two-down, sooty back-to-backs all over Britain. For years I thought our house was proper and normal, no different from anybody else's including Old Man Forsey's and the King's. I pictured His Majesty in a gold tub before the fire playing with diamond-encrusted submarines and the Queen singing on the lav at the bottom of their huge garden before tugging the gold chain. Mam kept the home spotless but was not happy about the way things were. She shattered my illusions and opened a window on another world – the world of the rich with their long deep baths, running hot water and lavs at the top of the stairs. Slowly it dawned on me that people actually lived like the famous I saw in the Hollywood films at the Bug House.

"And look what they did when the miners went on strike," Mam said bitterly to Mrs Penk during one of the many doorstep debates. "Brought in the bloody police and broke them. Them who live outside the valleys don't know the real price of coal."

"True," said Mrs Meredith whose husband was Welsh and had come south in the depression.

"Their wives've got fur coats though," Mrs Penk snapped,

and I thought Mam was going to rip off her face.

"Silly cow," she hissed, packing so much venom into the insult that Mrs Penk beat a hasty retreat.

I remember being told of great uncles that died of pneumoconiosis or allied lung diseases.

"They used to wander round the village in the daytime," she said, trying to stop her lower lip from quivering. "Faces as yellow as hens' feet and coughing their life away. Forty bloody years old and dead on their pins."

Then the tears flowed and she held me close, letting the grief triumph. Today she still maintains whenever the miners strike they are striking for the ghosts who paid the real price of coal, and I cannot return to South Wales without the echo of her words following me through the valleys.

* * *

"Why d'you get up so early, son?" Dad said, lacing his boots in the candlelit kitchen. "You're like a titchy little tom cat."

I grinned through the steam of my porridge.

"A little back-alley tom," he repeated, hating the prospect of the building site and the cold, damp darkness. He would have liked to have stayed by the fire carving animals from limewood or just reading.

"Go up Penks, and get me some tobacco," he added absently. Mam was singing "There'll be bluebirds over the white cliffs of Dover, tomorrow just you wait and see". The coal shovel grated and rasped over cinders and ash and banged against the back of the hearth. I opened the front door, letting in the breath of the new day and the catty stink of front gardens which were no bigger than billiard tables and were separated from the houses by a cobbled path.

Norah Skinner was filling the jug on our step from her milk can.

"Mornin'," she chirped – a plump, jolly girl belted into an old mac and sporting a brown tam. I walked up the terrace beside her.

"Mr Forsey's pixie didn take a stroll last night did 'er, Bri?" she winked.

"Dunno, Norah," I grinned.

"You'm a lil devil, dang me if you idn! What you goin' to be whain you grow up?"

"A wolf hunter."

"Get home do! – there idn no wolves in Debn."

"There's some up on Dartmoor. Mam says so."

The rest of her cheerful tittle-tattle passed over me for I was stalking the snowy hills of Scotland, a deerhound at my side and nothing but birds and animals and open country stretching before me, endlessly. . . .

Rain rolled off the surrounding hills and the blocked guttering above the living room window overflowed. I sat by the fire listening to the splat of water in the yard and drew birds on pieces of wallpaper and re-read the exciting parts of *Kidnapped*. Later, there was a knock at the front door and the sound of voices after Mam had opened it. Then she came and stood silently before the fire and I waited for her to speak.

"Auntie Avril's dead," she said quietly. "Cancer of the breast. Jesus Christ! – there's a terrible way to go. And she wasn't forty. Poor Avril."

She read the telegram again and placed it carefully behind the clock on the mantelpiece to show Dad when he came home from work.

"What's cancer, Mam?"

"A filthy disease. It eats your insides."

I drew my knees up to my chin feeling the horror squirm like a mess of cold eels in my belly. Hideous things were always carrying grown-ups off to the grave. If you stayed young you could avoid most of them. O God, I prayed, let Peter Pan come to my window tonight. Let me fly to the island where only good things happen.

Auntie Avril was really Dad's second cousin. She had been the sub-postmistress of a hamlet on the edge of Dartmoor. Three days later we caught the train to Moretonhampstead and were met at the station by the widower who drove us to the hamlet in his bread van.

"A sad do, Stan," Dad said.

"Er's better off now, Perce," came the morose reply.

Fog swirled and twisted over the drystone walls and banks of scrub beech. Ponies wandered across the road, their coats sequinned with moisture. The sky pressed down and it began to rain.

"Rotten day," Dad said gruffly.

Stan nodded and sighed. His collar was too tight and the

sweat stood out on his face. Sitting behind them under shelves where the delicate aroma of loaves and buns lingered I wondered what sort of day was OK for funerals. Surely the grimmer the better. A fresh bright spring afternoon, full of colour and birdsong, would make death too mean to contemplate. Everything seemed to die in the autumn – leaves, flowers, insects, so why not people? This led me to consider the zoology and entomology of heaven. Were there rats in paradise? And were there spirit bluebottles? I asked Mam and she told me sharply to shut up.

We walked the few yards from Auntie's dark little house to the church. A cold wind whined around the granite tower and sang in the draughty corners of the nave and chancel. Relatives and friends of the deceased had arrived from all over Devon and I saw people I'd never met before or even knew existed. Everyone was staring rigidly straight ahead for fear of making a fool of themselves before so many critical eyes.

"Why don't they play the organ, Mam?"

"Because there isn't one," she whispered. "Funny sort of place this is."

Faintly across the wind clamour and the coughing and fidgeting came the cello song of the churchyard trees. The door had been opened to admit the coffin, then closed and the pall-bearers were marching down the aisle. Like the other children I was fascinated by the ritual of death, and craned my neck to watch the box with Auntie in it being carried solemnly to the chancel and the waiting priest. One of the pall-bearers was shorter than his three companions and was out of step and no matter how hard he struggled to retrieve the situation the coffin's progress became jerkier and jerkier as though the poor little man had chosen the worst possible moment to learn the foxtrot. I caught cousin Jean's eye and we giggled but managed to stifle the sound by pinching our noses. The coffin wobbled past our pew with shortie frantically trying to control his feet. Then the man behind him trod on his heel and a small black shoe spun heavenwards and clacked down hard on the tiles. Shortie was wearing green socks and the one we would see had a hole through which poked an inch of pink big toe. The sweating, out-of-step unfortunate now had a queer, lopsided gait to add to his misery and our glee. A glance around me confirmed my suspicions. Nearly all the children were staring down at their shoes, shoulders shaking, and so were many of the adults.

Cousin Jean showed me a red, tear-stained face, a picture of wild mirth strangled by guilt where self-control was fighting a losing battle. I couldn't hold it back any longer but still had the sense to try and disguise the noise.

Laughter erupted in a great, spluttering snort. For one horrific moment a green bubble swelled from my right nostril but Mam burst it with the fingers of the hand she had clamped over my mouth. Then her free hand clenched on the scruff of my neck and I was propelled up the aisle and out into the grey, windy day for the hiding of my life.

No matter how hard I tried I could not imagine let alone share Uncle Stan's grief. It had rutted and pinched the suet pudding of his face and he was dredging up his loneliness un-ashamedly, sob upon sob. But I had my own problems. After standing shivering in the porch for the remainder of the service, I must have been a pathetic little figure, the sort of skin-and-bone kid Victorians would have paid good money to have had at the heart of their funerals.

A few of the mourners gave me stony looks as if I had scripted the Pall-Bearer sketch. The rain stopped and the fog lifted but the sun refused to shine. We followed the coffin to the freshly dug grave, under the stunted beech trees and the wide-branched yew. Starlings and fieldfares bent the twigs above me and a blackbird sang from the top of the celtic cross by the lych gate.

> "As doves to the whitest houses soonest come,
> So the Holy God makes cleanest hearts his home"

read the inscription on the nearest tombstone. Lead lettering braided with orange and pale green rosettes of lichen. I was captivated by the After-Life Advertising, by epigrams like:

> "Then ask'st what years thou hast. I answer None.
> For what thou hadst, thou hast not; they be gone."

A kind of animal terror loosened my bowels when I was led to the graveside. Then I really pitied Auntie Avril. She was lying in a wooden box being lowered into a black hole, and a little later a man was shovelling earth into the hole and soon Auntie Avril was gone forever. So, that was death – cold, wet, grey weather, silent people, black ties, black soil, black nothingness. Why didn't the birds stop singing out of respect? Why did the raindrops twinkle on leaves and cousin Jean's hair and the blades of grass? Nature's indifference to the human condition chilled me more than anything until I grew older and began to look beyond self.

Among the grey buildings of Dartmoor granite was the sudden dazzle of a white cottage. I sat in the window of the house that did not smell friendly and drank the strange-tasting tea and ate the beef sandwiches and fairy cakes. Above the barns and stables and clumps of trees, the moors vanished dark and seductive into mist.

Dad joined me, a glass of brown ale held elegantly to his lips, crumbs on his chin and the lapels of his jacket. The sad, wet afternoon had robbed him of wisecracks and banter. It was the first time I had seen the jester without his cap-of-bells.

4
Down the Bright Stream

More often than not it rained on Guy Fawkes Night, but for once
a fine crisp day ended optimistically under clear skies. All week
the juvenile pyromaniacs of the Devonport Inn district had been
building a bonfire big enough to barbecue a brace of dinosaurs.
The older kids mounted guard after dark in case someone tried to
light it early, but these precautions were of no avail. On the
morning of November 5th the police, fire brigade and a posse of
council workmen stormed the St Michael's Road playing field
and reduced the mountain of tinder from the size of Woolworths
to a mere double-decker.

Our effort was more modest – just a mess of sticks, broken
furniture, boxes, straw, newspapers, a dead Lawson cypress, Mr
Penk's backgate which he never missed till the following morning, a tractor tyre, Colin Yeo's cat, Bonzo, that had been killed
by a car and was stretched out stiff in a shoebox waiting for the
Viking send-off, and an old kennel lifted from the Gowman
backyard, and all piled up in the lane at the bottom of the
terrace.

Down by the railway the accountant who lived behind
wrought iron gates and hedges of box and privet was giving a
firework party for the little lah-di-dahs that went to local
private schools like Cavendish College and said "thenks"

instead of "thanks" and were ever ready with a "wow" of amazement or a breezy "gosh". O'Flaherty had "invited" Colin, Soapy Tucker and me to watch the revelry from an ornamental fir near the greenhouse. We were reluctant to accept because Horseshit was perpetually questing for trouble and bonfire night was a big occasion, especially after the war years. Everything the cockney monster touched fell apart or rotted or blew up.

The party was an "oos" and "ahs" affair, all pretty-pretties and the fizz and flare of gunpowder magicked into rainbows. Not a banger was to be heard until O'Flaherty lobbed three Boy Scout Rousers among the innocents and ran for it. Scuttling up the road after the others I felt a pang of remorse. I liked Mr Abrahams the accountant. He had caught me scrumping apples in his garden and had smiled and opened the gate for me, saying I was free to help myself whenever I pleased, providing I came to the front door and was polite. And I envied the children round the little bonfire making circles in the darkness with their sparklers. They weren't forever at each other's throats, and the pleasant, easy-going atmosphere suggested order and belonging.

Naturally O'Flaherty was not content to enjoy a normal, rowdy November 5th. Miss Millman caught him dragging her hallstand out the front door, and Mr Gowman, answering her squawks, had great difficulty separating the arsonist from his piece of illicit kindling. But the O'Flaherty would not be fobbed-off with Beryl Eccles's Rowton House Guy. He and some cronies forced little Barry Salter to nick his mother's beaver-lamb coat and Robin Hood hat which was the height of female fashion. Then he dressed the Guy and sat it on an old cane chair and had it secured to the top of the bonfire. From the ground it looked like Mrs Salter. She was a peroxide blonde frump pushing forty, with a broad Slavonic face and big red lips. Maybe Beryl had her in mind when she was painting the features on the white paper bag before pulling it over the turnip head.

"Mrs Salter will kill you," she said, gazing proudly at her handiwork. We were all scared of the consequences but ached to see Worzel Gummidge's sister go up in smoke.

"She won't notice the coat," Barry said hoarsely. "She won't . . . will her?"

"Wanna bet?" said O'Flaherty, and he grinned the sort of grin you would expect to find under a leather hood in the torture chambers of the Spanish Inquisition.

"Come on, Horseshit," I mumbled. "It idn fair."

"Shut . . . your . . . cake-hole, Carter."

His lips still curved upwards but the little piggy eyes had become grey pebbles of malice. For a moment we stared at each other. The darkness was loud and alive with muffled bangs and the plup of bursting rockets. And standing there, fists clenched, I knew I would have to challenge O'Flaherty one day if only to punch the hatred and the hurt out of my system before I went down.

"You seen my Barry?" Mrs Salter said. She stood next to Beryl and Butch Meredith, under the chestnut trees right in front of the bonfire. Barry darted down the lane and ran home to hide under his bed. The first of our rockets whooshed out of the milk bottles and O'Flaherty struck a match and put it to the wood-shavings. The flames leapt and flickered and illumined the Guy. Mrs Fawkes sat grinning mindlessly from her cane chair, a very affluent figure for such a backstreet occasion.

"Barry," Mrs Salter called, peering down the lane as more children arrived carrying torches and sparklers.

"Co-ee, Barry."

"Barry made the Guy," O'Flaherty said. "We didn't know he was so clever."

Mrs Salter's eyes smilingly strayed to the effigy that was the clone of her Saturday Night self. The flames' progress was halted briefly by a big, damp armchair.

"Ere!" she shrieked. "That's my bloody best coat!"

And she picked up a bucket and tossed the contents on the fire. It was paraffin. Johnny Pym and Mr Gowman made token gestures and tried to scale the funeral pyre but the heat drove them back.

"I'll flay that little bugger," cried Mrs Salter. "By Christ – I'll have him if it's the last thing I do. I'll swing for him."

Flames licked at the beaverlamb. The Robin Hood hat, the paper bag face and the straw hair blazed and vanished. Then the centre of the fire collapsed and the furcoated Mrs Fawkes was gone.

"It wudn even paid for," said Mrs Salter.

By now no one was laughing and O'Flaherty had melted into the darkness.

"Little swine," Mrs Salter sobbed. "I bet you lot made him do it. Why'd you keep pickin' on Barry? You put him up to it. Bloody gangsters."

She turned fiercely on us, balling her fists and waving them about her head.

"Not my Brian," Mam said.

"O no – not him," came the sarcastic reply. "It couldn't be him. The sun shines out his arse, don't it. Anyway, the police'll get to the bottom of it."

"What? – his arse?" said Colin Yeo and Mrs Salter had to be restrained.

Half an hour later PC Budworth's bicycle was seen against the Salters' garden wall. But Barry never split. He had no desire to spend the rest of his schooldays hounded by the mad O'Flaherty.

*   *   *

The baker's roundsman called three times a week and Mam had two large whites at fourpence halfpenny a loaf. She never ran up bills. It was cash on the nail or we went without. Debt was the blackest sin, after adultery and idleness.

On Mondays and Fridays Fred Stone came to the door selling rabbits. If we bought one on Monday Mam would prepare it for the midweek stew. Friday's rabbit would end up in Saturday's pie or baked on Sunday. She made me a Davy Crockett cap out of coney fur and Dad could fashion really good bows with taut string that didn't go plunk! in a limp ineffective way like other kids' bowstrings. He was very proud of his trade.

"Jesus Christ was a carpenter," he said.

We were walking home past St Andrew's Church after a Sunday stroll along Goodrington beach. People were gathering for evensong.

"A carpenter," Dad repeated – "not a bank manager or a hotelier or a stockbroker."

He chose to ignore Jesus's main role as Son of God and the Saviour of Mankind. For Dad it was Jesus Christ, carpenter and spare-time Messiah, the original Working Class hero.

I took my bow and arrows of ash and hazel out where late autumn was stripping the countryside of its last secrets. At dimpsey flocks of oystercatchers settled on the water meadows as I threaded through Clennon's reeds. But one sunny day I went further than I had ever been before. I left the valley around breakfast time and crossed the Old Brixham Road into the farmland off Litstone. A line of women picking potatoes moved up the field beside the lane, silently, their heads bowed and nothing but the rattle of potatoes in the pails to mark their progress. The mild weather had left a few leaves on the oaks and there were still crimson cider apples hanging from the trees in sheltered, bracken-choked goyals. Woodpigeons settled on the winter wheat and big gangs of foreign thrushes plundered the hedgerow wealth.

The hilltop spinneys had been planted decades ago to the glory of God – or so I thought because they were like domed cathedrals. I did not know about the pheasant slaughter industry and the need for coverts. I had convinced myself that old foxes came there to die. Creeping through the trees I was King Arthur's champion wolf hunter and all the dawns and dimpseys yet to come would open into Avalon. The modern age would never hold me in chains. It was no more than a dream lapping at the margins of the eternal dream. The past – the beautiful deathless country of oakwoods and pine forests, moorlands, swift rivers and hills rolling away to the bottom of the sky. And the sea which was only five minutes down the road from our house played its part but did not tug at my imagination or exercise the magic of open countryside.

Pestilence, cruelty and poverty were absent from my Dream Kingdom but sometimes Death riding a puma and looking like a tubercular O'Flaherty leapt out of a nightmare and dragged me screaming and kicking from under the bedclothes.

By the bank near Litstone ford I found a dead badger in a snare. The wire had chewed through the coarse hair to open the flesh around its neck and throat. The flyblown animal had dug a hole eighteen inches deep in its frenzy for life. Its claws were blunt and muddy and it lay nose buried in front paws as if it had perished of despair. I stroked it but did not cry. The misery went too deep for tears although the pain and anger and horror were a sickness in my guts like the distress I felt when I saw cattle being driven through the gates of the Crown and Anchor abattoir, lowing and jostling, their eyes full of terror and bewilderment. But why a badger?

"They make shaving brushes out of their bristles," Dad said unhappily.

"I idn going to shave when I grow up."

"Colin Yeo snares rabbits," Dad said. "Rabbits get throttled but that don't seem to worry you."

"We eat rabbits," I said, as if it justified the whole ugly business of catching living creatures in wires. I had to defend it because I participated in it.

"We eat sheep and cows. So I suppose it's alright to strangle them to death," Dad said, but seeing the hurt in my eyes he added: "anyway, it could've been worse. It could have been a gin."

Mam, who had been brought up in a water bailiff's cottage on the banks of the River Wye, was not impressed by his logic. Her love of nature rarely admitted sentimentality. Meat was meat and the Morgans had lived through hard times.

Huge flocks of birds were filling the sky to the west. On the hill above Lower Well Farm I cut a swede and hacked out a feed of juicy white wedges. Against the ash poles below was the steaming thatch of a cottage. The pig pens and chicken runs of the smallholding were scattered along the coombe and geese were grazing the sward beneath cider apple trees on both sides of the brook. In the neck of the coombe a man was laying the hedge watched by a couple of Welsh collies. The smoke from his bonfire lofted blue into blue. I descended cautiously, remembering I was the Celtic hunter approaching the Saxon farm. A dog barked, someone clanked a pail and the stream sang through the morning. Then I smelt frying bacon and everything in the valley assumed the strangeness of hurdy-gurdy music. I loved the sky and the hills and trees, and the creatures whose presence was printed on the fabric of the new day. I loved the thick, leaf-strewn grass and the sparkling brook, but most of all I loved the outdoor life and Devon.

Trying to cross the brook on stepping stones which were under water I slipped and went in above the knees. This gave me the excuse to wade downstream, my hob-nailed boots finding plenty of purchase among the storm debris. Now I was truly part of the landscape. Foxes and horses took to the water but civilized folk shunned it unless they were well protected from its coldness and wetness. But my senses lusted after total knowledge of the wild places. When I died at some impossibly distant moment I hoped my bones would be scattered on a high hill, like the bones of a crow, to melt into the beloved country. Please God, I prayed, let me lie on a high hill, not in a cemetery.

The brook was full of the sky where it flowed through open fields. It was alive, too, with its own light and the flat reaches glittered like cellophane. I waded through pools the colour of barley wine or scrumpy or milkless tea, depending on how much light they held. The stickleback swims were swollen with last night's rain, and the spate carried a froth like Old Man's Beard from the shallows where claws of water flashed and blinked.

Little nuggets of sunshine glinted from drifts of grit and pebbles, and small shadows glided and flickered into deeper unmoving shadow. Beneath the dazzle and spangle the fish skimmed along the smooth dark silt and hung in the transparent gloom, tails twitching. Every so often the water gurgled under a tangle of brambles, pushed against the bank and looped around my legs.

Under the trees it was horsechestnut-brown and my passing released puffs of silt. Alders and hazels arched over the brook. A robin sang, woodpigeons crooned, but mantling everything was the soft, fluorescent noise of water, lisping and twinkling down to the River Dart.

A farm cat trotted up to me at Port Bridge. I sat on the parapet, wringing out my socks and emptying my boots. The beagles had met near Waddeton and were busy drawing the wide pastures overlooking the Dart. The cat dug its claws into my bare knees and stood on its hindlegs, struggling to place its nose against mine which is the animal way of kissing.

"Dear lil pussy," I crooned, easing the tiny scimitars out of my flesh.

"Lil pussy has been mousing, hasn't he? Who's a good pussy – yes, lovely black pussy."

"He brings home fowls and conies and all sorts," said a voice.

An old lady had emerged from the house over the road. She was small, weasel-eyed and had a huge goitre. The cigarette wedged in the corner of her mouth was adding its invisible contribution of nicotine to the yellow stain on the fuzz of her upper lip.

"Ben's a lil heller for fowls."

The broad Devon accent hardened the "f" to a "v" and "fowls" became "vowulls".

" 'Er's had ducks, too, and hares and 'er brings home partridges and pheasants."

Objects were "he", never "it", and persons irrespective of sex were always "her". Thus "*he*'s a boodivull (beautiful) lil kettle." The classic piece of pure Devon was "he's a she bain 'er" and was commonly used in sexing puppies or kittens, and indicated the female.

"Do 'ee like this girt (great) lump on me neck?" the old lady suddenly flung at me.

I shook my head.

"Idn 'er just the maister of all lumps", and she sighed smoke and drew her fingernails delicately across the surface of the swelling.

"Have you got something in your throat, missus?"

She laughed and looked down at my sodden boots and said:

"Your Dad will belt 'ee. Why idn 'ee at school?"

"I'm ill."

"Get home do, boy! Look at the colour in your cheeks. You'm as red as a chimbley pot. There's nort wrong with 'ee."

"I got shell shock."

The goitre throbbed when she laughed.

"Idn you a bliddy lil romancer. Could 'ee eat a bit of fruit cake and drink a cup of tea? Best dry they boots or you'll catch rheumatics. My Albert was bent zo bad whain he died they had to bury un in a box shaped like a banana."

The sight of my eyes growing large and round had her wheezing and coughing and jigging up and down. She put my boots on the range and my socks in the oven, wrapped in brown paper, while I wolfed a great slab of Dundee cake and was introduced to a Jack Russell called Smutz who had a disturbing grin and cabriole backlegs.

"I zeed a girt otter in the creek," she said. "He got a fish. Lovely old boy he was, too. Have you ever zin a otter?"

Once, I told her, in Paignton harbour.

"Twudn no otter," she snorted. "That was a seal. Otters don't like salt water – it hurts their eyes."

I didn't bother to argue. She was like the poacher Tacker Willock who believed the rats living on the sea cliffs above Crystal Cave at Broadsands were water rats. The wildlife book illustrations carried no weight. Books were suspect, occult devices to many members of a class denied higher education. Ignorance therefore prevailed and was passed on from generation to generation.

"Walk down the creek, ma boodie," the old lady continued. "Maybe you'll zee a real otter. And you come back next week and us'll have another chin wag."

But the goitre scared me and I never visited her house again. I saw her only once more and that was in Litstone Lane towards the end of winter. She looked sick and worn-out and was talking to herself. I should not have run away when she called out but the grotesque purple lump sent me scooting off through the trees. Beryl Eccles was to blame. She said goitres were catching, like mumps.

"Humpty Dumpty had one on his back," said Dad, and Mam laughed so much she spilt a little hot custard on Nibs's head and the cat did three noisy high speed circuits of the kitchen.

"You stay away from the old witch," Mam said. "Or she'll turn you into a frog."

"And you'll go round speaking funny like that onion seller from Britanny," Dad said.

Their prejudices won and the poor, lonely old lady was soon forgotten in my pursuit of excitement and fresh countryside.

*   *   *

There were no otters in Stoke Gabriel Creek that morning but shoals of mullet cruised around and a heron fished the shallows beneath the oaks opposite the church. Gently the fish dimpled the surface and the black headed gulls gave Punch and Judy cries, wheeling and diving by the dam. Then a cloud of white doves clattered from the church tower and landed among the tombstones. A man was shaking pieces of bread from a bag, his face lifted skywards looking like a Sunday School St Francis.

I climbed the hedge of wild clematis, hazels and briars, tugging off handfuls of white awns and pulling the scarlet hips for catapult ammunition. Beyond the dam and the sluice the tidal reach of the Dart was a prairie of sunlight, shifting and shimmering, briefly holding the images of birds and boats. Among the twisted and polished oak roots of the point, my boots skidding on the bladderwrack, I gazed across the river and felt good. This was where the curlews came after they had passed over my home. Here I would find the seeds of poems and stories and, more important, a permanent spiritual anchorage.

5

Frost Patterns

I tried to read an abridged *Bevis* but Richard Jefferies' cream-puff boy 'hero' was too sweet for my palate and the language too precious – unlike Arthur Ransome's *Great Northern*. But I could relate to the crowstarver in Henry Williamson's story of that name when Dad read it to me. I had built a little fire of dry leaves and twigs in the hilltop spinney above Berry Pomeroy and had enjoyed the clear twilight with the cold intensifying and the barn owls screaming across the rickyards. I knew the worth of being alone on a hill after dark listening to what the night had to say. The universe drew my thoughts and made me go to the books to discover the names of galaxies, stars and constellations. It was like loving a girl. You had to find out her name and let the emotions work on it and lend it lustre.

Aldebaran, Sirius, Vega, Canes Venatici; the Plough, the Bear, the Dog Star. Nights of ravishing beauty and the rabbits lying stiff with fear in the snares and the gin holding the fox by the leg.

December was electrifying. Days closed swiftly, dark, sleet-rattled, and opened white and still. At dimpsey the starlings roared over the copse and the scarecrow amongst the kale looked ready to come to life. The grin on its mangold face oozed menace, and I would creep past the old dawbake, catapult

loaded, prepared to sink a pebble between its deep-cut, trian-
gular eyes. But at the table before a fire of ash logs was the
greatest thrill of all. My knife released a plume of fragrance from
the jacket potato and the butter trickled into steaming pockets
of goodness. Then Nibs would rise and shake herself so that her
ears clacked, arch her back, yawn and extend her front legs in a
quivering stretch before scrounging from my plate.

Once the tea things were cleared away Dad took up his
carving tools and began coaxing a wild animal or a bird out of
wood. He was very gifted and told me he saw the fox standing
there inside the block of walnut and all he had to do was set it
free. Every beautiful thing he made went for beer – fox and
mallard, heron and trout, shire horse, badger baited by terriers.
Nothing remained as a testament to his artistic ability. Visitors
were expected to gauge his talent from the terrible watercolour
of a hunt scene hanging over the sideboard.

Christmas was less than a week away and Dad's carving was
stepped-up and the objets d'art translated into bottles of port,
whisky and ale. Carol singers from other neighbourhoods sometimes strayed down the terrace and if O'Flaherty and his mob
were absent survived to murder the first verse of "Good King
Wenceslas" before hammering on our door to go through their
awful "We wish you a Merry Christmas" routine. Dad was daft
enough to cough-up ninepence or one-and-three, and even
dafter to entrust me with the dispensing of largesse. If the singers
were big I'd give them threepence and pocket the silver; if they
were small I'd tell them quietly to bugger off and drown their
response by bawling Merry Christmas and slamming the door.
On a particularly memorable occasion a dozen of us, including
the O'Flaherty, ambushed a rival gang outside Miss Millman's
and forced them to listen to our tom cat rendering of "God Rest
Ye Merry Gentlemen" while they fed the revenue of their own
night's work into our cocoa tin. Very few carolling entrepren-
eurs ventured down the terrace after that.

Christmas gave my country wanderings fresh purpose. Dad
supplied the tree, we got a seven shilling capon from Skinner's
Dairy, and I guaranteed the holly. But the urban would keep
intruding in the shape of the school inspector with the withered
arm. He called for the last time after seeing me in St Michael's
butcher's one afternoon. Mam had patiently reminded him of
my malady for over three years but he kept knocking at the door

and bothering her. In the end she gripped him by the throat and breathed fire and Welsh obscenities onto his head. And he skipped away, eyes bulging and glasses steamed up, trying to salvage his dignity with a couple of half-hearted threats.

"Cheeky rat," Mam fumed. "Standing on my own doorstep and calling me a liar. "Duw! Duw! – there's a worm for you."

But she was not proud of bullying the little man.

"Him and his withered arm," she murmured, the anger leaving her eyes. "Now don't get under my feet, Brian. Go and find something to do while I hang out the washing!" Dad was having toe rag for tea and she put the dried fish to soak in the saucepan. The washing was done in the sink and was a long, tedious chore, and I got on her nerves. So I stuffed the packet of beef dripping sandwiches into the pocket of my jerkin and went to Clennon, withdrawing from the world of school inspectors, washdays and shopping. I found beauty enough among the pigsties, hen houses and cattlesheds where the Wessex saddleback, Black Minorcas and White-faced Herefords fulfilled their lowly destinies. The sparrow hawk smashing through the hazel twigs to snatch the chaffinch excited me more than anything that happened on a football pitch or at the cinema. Hawks and falcons had wicked eyes and the yellow rings around them make them look insane. But O'Flaherty's eyes were the most disturbing. They had blood in them, like Bickford's bull, and they never registered fear.

Mr Brinham the cowman was the tied tenant of Mill Marsh Cottage. The austere stone building guarded the entrance to Ladder Lane. Mr Brinham was a short, polite man whose customary work clothes were gaiters, cord breeches and a waistcoat. When it rained he tied a sack to his waist to keep his knees dry and slung another round his shoulders. He had the solemn leathery face of a reservation indian.

For forty-two shillings a week he was expected to put in long hours and never had more than four days off a year. Farmer Bickford demanded and got his pound of flesh and little love was lost between the stoical labourer and his boss. Mrs Brinham walked fifty yards to the farmyard tap several times a day for water, and on Mondays when she was washing for nine, eighteen gallons had to be carried back to the cottage. Farmer Bickford would ride past her on his horse as if she weren't there, afraid of her tongue and unwilling to meet eyes brimming with resentment.

"Stingy old pig," she'd mutter. "Tidn right. Tidn proper."

Marriage and motherhood for most working-class women meant at the very least forty years of unbroken drudgery. Everything around them conspired to make life a penance – the lack of facilities, their role as bed warmer, cook, washerwoman, waitress, housekeeper and gardener, all on a pittance and with little to brighten the monotony. A man acquired a beast of burden at the altar and nowhere did beauty fade so fast as on the face of a labourer's wife. Their damp, gloomy cottages were put up by moral bankrupts whose hand could be seen in the savage game laws. Yet Jerusalem might have been built here if love and compassion had prevailed amongst those born to wealth and power. For every good master there are three greedy idiots. The memory of the true gentleman endures but his benign despotism which should have become the criterion of all private and state land management died with him and was covered with an ocean of mediocrity.

"You'm still home from school, then," said Mrs Brinham. "You'm like a ferret the way you'm in and out of everywhere."

I could manage to carry half a bucket of water and my two trips saved her one. The cattle sliding and stumbling down the hill announced milking time and her husband's homecoming.

"I've got a helper," she said.

"Us'll have to put up his wages," smiled Mr Brinham.

"Double nort is nort," she said. But I had some clotted cream and sugar on bread and a glass of homemade barley water.

I hung around the cottage and the farm buildings and made friends with everyone because of the animals. What the labourer took for granted I considered a privilege – riding Bathsheba, driving the cattle into the shippen, counting the dead chickens after the hunt rode through. The splendour presiding over the farm touched my life but the grinding toil of the farmworker's lot remained an alien adult preserve. I saw the cheerful, sunny face of rural Devon and everything around me became part of my game. Those kind working men and women put up with me and let me build my fantasies around their daily lives. But they sensed I was an observer, always there on the edge yet never truly belonging, like Van Gogh in the olive groves of Arles or Coleridge in the Lake District.

The wonder lay in a multitude of simple experiences: splashing through the water of a flooded lane; lifting the skulls of weasels and stoats from the keeper's gibbet; watching the lazy curve of the catapult pebble bounce a sparrow off the chimney pot; standing among horses in the stable; the sight of hounds running at full cry along the brow of Cider Mill Hill.

Now that the war was over the hunt flashed in and out of my life. I was too small to keep up on foot and the meets were rarely close enough to home for me to get involved. But occasionally I'd hear the yelp of a horn and the pack giving tongue, and catch a glimpse of pink on shadowy farmland and see horses and riders silhouetted against the sky.

My sympathies like those of the other children I knew were with the fox, and I was deeply suspicious of those well-breeched men and women braying over my head in light saloon bar accents. Wherever they gathered I smelt violence of a dark, pagan kind. Up Stuggy Lane I encountered bloodlust like the raw ache of winter. Grim-faced women on huge horses milled around. The hounds were singing and the riders whooping. Then something small and torn and bloody was swung aloft above the steaming dogs and the chase was over.

"Open the gate, boy."

And I did, although my cheeks were burning and I wanted to growl "piss off". I could not understand why posh grown-ups were allowed to hunt an animal to death. My peasant breeding did not help. It was difficult to look up at a man on a horse without the desire to drag him off. Later I found a different atmosphere at the great Dartmoor meets where the killing of a fox was not perverted to a gory, society caper. And I also learned that the hounds dealt death swiftly, not like the snare, the gin or the badly aimed buckshot. I shed many prejudices when I got to know Claude Whitley, Master of the South Devon Hunt. Gradually I came to see that good human beings were not the product or the monopoly of any particular class. But at the age of nine everything registered in black and white. The sleek, red fox was born to freedom and I loved him and my heart leapt whenever I saw him flattening over field walls or running through the bracken into Clennon Woods. His enemies were my enemies and because they came from another class they were easy to misunderstand and dislike.

My admiration for the fox has persisted. So many hands are

raised against him – gamekeeper, poultryman, farmer, hunts-
man, trapper; his kind are poisoned, gassed, shot, trapped and
run to death by hounds. Yet he remains a fugitive spirit, symbol-
izing the plight of all wild creatures that fail to fit comfortably
into Man's world.

*   *   *

In the days before bacon and egg pie became quiche lorraine and
the only double yellow lines on the road were the queues of
Japanese tourists outside Madame Tussaud's I heard a rail call
from Clennon's reeds. Nature and Man had contrived to make
over the eons a valley of extraordinary loveliness. Or maybe
I worshipped it as I worshipped Mam, refusing to see imper-
fection. Frost turned the apple trees and clamps of roots and
stable-top dovecotes into the fantastic set of some Russian
ballet. Then the robin's whispered song was audible a hundred
yards up Stuggy Lane through the white powdery hush. Partridges sheltered behind the ricks and hundreds of woodpigeons
rushed over the deep-banked lanes.

> Lovely are the curves of the white owl sweeping wavy in
> the dusk lit by one large star.

Yes, the owls of Broome linhay belonged to frosty dusks and
without them the valley would have been impoverished. I knew
I'd hear them as I crunched through the cat ice, shouldering
a great bundle of holly. Holly, frost and owls, like an RSPB
Christmas card, but Dad's world of hops and malt and cider
apples could eclipse it. Christmas Eve was the glittering prize at
the end of the year. Nothing could spoil it. Dad and Uncle Frank
pubcrawled themselves silly, and Mam sang to the mince pies in
the kitchen that had become Aladdin's cave, and the pub was a
galleon full of laughter and drunken pirates who had slipped out
of their cycle clips and marriages for the evening.

Soon I had forgotten my vows to the horses and the foxes.
The frost patterns on the windows were beautiful, but they
were outside, and Christmas was the family happening, as un-
ashamedly pagan as the mistletoe in the hall.

6
Tacker

'The vicar prefers his Three Nuns', read the pipe tobacco advert in the country magazine and I wondered why Mam and Dad nudged each other and laughed.

"Do you know the difference between an elephant's bum and a letter box?" Dad said, waving the envelope under my nose. I shook my head.

"Well, it's no use asking you to post this letter," he grinned.

Christmas had come and gone and for a while the first days of the New Year depressed me. But soon the North Easterly gales were bringing hordes of waders and wild fowl to Clennon, and groups of bramblings, fieldfares and redwings pattered down onto the water-meadows. Grandad said this meant a hard winter but he prophesied that every year and Gran would stare at him through pale lashes wondering why she had spent two thirds of her life with the self-opinionated old fool.

I loved her almost as much as I loved Mam. She was small and round faced and her hair was set in a neat silver bun. The sepia photograph on the mantelpiece was proof of the prettiness she possessed when young and it still shone through her old age like the moon through a cloud.

The lady's sewing maid had married the stern young carpenter and produced two sons – Dad and his elder brother Frank.

Their terrace house was a museum of Victorian and Edwardian
bits and pieces and Grandad's World War One memorabilia. The
old man had made a wireless the size of a tea chest which was
lost among the living room clutter that included an ornate
sideboard of amazing vulgarity and a massive framed print of
the play scene from *Hamlet*. Two-and-sixpenny wallpaper had
been hung downstairs and the one-and-eleven stuff upstairs. At
night the brass souvenirs Sergeant Carter had brought back from
France after fighting through the Great War unscathed gleamed
in the gas-light: shell cases, cigarette and tobacco tins fashioned
by German POW's, matchbox holders, paper-knives and candle-
sticks. Not much to show for nearly five years of trench warfare.
But he had some medals hidden in a chest in his bedroom which
he refused to display even on Remembrance Day. He regarded
those grim years as a personal experience and wouldn't let
anyone trespass on the memory. It was strange behaviour for a
man lacking imagination.

I was getting a shilling a week pocket money from Gran and a
few pence purchased a front seat at the Bug House Cinema on
Saturday evenings and the privilege of sampling movie fare like
Zoro, *Superman* and the singing cowboy westerns. We went in
a yodelling gang to swell the ranks of ruffians from all over
Paignton. Everybody who was anyone in the back street hier-
archy was there – except O'Flaherty. He had been banned for life
from the Bug House, the Regent and the Picture House for a
variety of misdemeanors. At the Bug House he had launched a
single-handed blitzkrieg on the commissionaire, an amiable
Goliath of an ex-bouncer nicknamed Kong after the famous
monkey. O'Flaherty had peppered Kong's head with hard green
gooseberries shot rapidly and with tremendous force from his
best catapult.

The other cinemas had black-balled Horseshit as a result of
this attack but the management of the Palladium showed remarkable naivity in giving him a second chance. They got him
in the office and made him swear to be on his best behaviour. It
was like making Burke or Hare a night nurse in an Edinburgh
geriatric ward. From high in the gods O'Flaherty bombed the
stalls, using ice-cream cones he had demanded with menace
from real children. Several strong men were required to prise
him out of the lavatory into the waiting arms of the law. And
although we booed and hissed his departure, we secretly re-

joiced knowing we could enjoy cinematic gems like *The Escape of Tarzan* and *Duck Soup* free of violent interruption.

*   *   *

Three tremendous events occurred in January 1947: Soapy Tucker's Dad came home from India, Constable Budworth died and I was accepted as Tacker Willock's unpaid assistant.

Mr Tucker had spent nearly all the war in a Japanese prisoner of war camp and had needed a long spell of convalescence to recover even partially from the ill-treatment. Some of us turned out to see his triumphant return but there was no band and no civic dignitaries at Paignton Station. The Tucker family walked up Elmsleigh Road and I had my first glimpse of the yellow, grinning, emaciated war hero Soapy had spoken of so often. I saw the skull face and the demob suit flapping on the skeleton, and I saw Mrs Tucker clinging to this apparition and kissing it but not as passionately as she had kissed the American soldiers she had picked up in the pubs during the war. She had been an outcast and Mr Tucker's homecoming brought her back into the community, tarnished and unforgiven yet secure provided she never strayed again.

The death of PC Budworth shocked the neighbourhood and most of the grown-ups attended his funeral and there was an obituary in the local paper. He had been greatly respected and his little acts of kindness and charity surfaced after the burial, things I never dreamt possible like helping war widows and speaking out for O'Flaherty when Reform School seemed inevitable. Because he had rarely smiled I failed to see the flicker of a soul in his eyes. He dropped dead of a heart attack while sawing logs for old Miss Millman and a week later we had a new, cheerful young beat bobby called PC Tarr who could out-run every kid, including Butch Meredith whose speed over a hundred yards was legendary.

"Doctor says you can go back to school," said Mam the morning after Constable Budworth's memorial service. We were trooping out of the surgery into a freezing mist that had brought the early traffic to a standstill but was showing signs of lifting.

"When?"

"Monday week."

I grinned up at her.

"Do you want to go, Bri?"

"Yes," I said honestly " – very much."

"Won't you miss your Mam?"

"I'll see you every morning and evening and all weekend."

"You'll never stop loving your Mam will you Bri?"

The question was so stupid I couldn't reply. I just clung to her hand, shaking my head, waiting for the cold to stop pinching my ears.

"Wrap up warm if you're going out," she continued, wiping the dewdrop from the tip of my nose. "Why don't you stay by the fire and draw? I'll buy you some marshmallows."

"Uncle Tacker promised me a rabbit if I helped him."

"That Tacker," she snorted. "Him and his rotten ferrets."

But like Dad she had a soft spot for the old villain and enjoyed his company over a drink on Friday nights. I think he was a distant cousin of my father although it was never confirmed because of Tacker's disreputable past. He was a sixty-year-old widower, the youngest of seven brothers. Blinking from behind national health glasses were small, milky blue eyes and when he grinned he displayed a mouth full of gums and one or two teeth. A "tacker" is a little boy and Uncle Harold may have been this at some time or other but I remember above everything else his intimidating bulk and the rapid, broad Devon of his speech. Few men could survive that verbal torrent. In his prime he had been one of the town's best fighters and was always prepared to back up hot words with fists the size of sheeps' skulls.

Being a poacher meant status among his working class contemporaries and quite a few middle class romantics smiled benignly on Tacker. Richard Jefferies would have done the usual cosmetic surgery on a similar figure before releasing it into the pages of his rural fairy tales. Tacker had risen from Nature and returned to it because it held all he loved but he was not a velveteen Pimpernel ghosting around the copses by starlight, fighting gamekeepers and knocking down policeman in job-lots. Nor did he leave trout at the vicarage door or a pheasant in the magistrate's porch. He gave nothing away and was as vicious as he was hard, but like many thieves he had a certain charm and was warm towards those he loved although I rarely heard him speak kindly to his daughter, Midge.

Tacker was a true native of the West Country. His days were coloured by the seasons and his tune measured by the fall of leaves, the budding of primroses, in haymaking, harvest and the misery of swede cutting, and in the opening and closing of the pub door. But he wasn't a Devonshire Thoreau and was untroubled by any desire to distil his experiences into art or philosophy. If anything he was a solitary who lived yet did not revere the land between the lower Dart and the sea.

"Hark at they bliddy old scritch owulls."

"Where be 'em to, Tacker?" I asked.

"Down yonder by the farm."

"I saw one up over the hill last night."

"They'm buggers for rats," Tacker said, and he belched cider fumes. Billy the lurcher nuzzled the poacher's fingers and Tacker told the dog not to fret because he was "a prapper boy" and "a girt vool" and "a gewd dug". He loved it more than he loved his daughter, Midge.

I was at Tacker's house the following day, on the heels of sunrise. He was sinking his naked feet into a pair of pre-war wellingtons and had lit the gas under a saucepan of milk. I opened the back door and waited for him to ask me in. The kitchen smelt like a fox's earth.

"I'm buggered if you idn keener than Ladyship," he said, referring to his working jill.

I grinned and bent over Billy, and the lurcher flashed me a sideways glance and thumped the floor with his tail.

"Habn you got no home to go to, Carter?" said Midge.

She came downstairs in her dad's khaki greatcoat and spooned Camp coffee into a couple of dirty mugs.

"You'm as mazed as father." Mazed was Devonian for mad and was considered a tremendous insult.

"Go and get Ladyship, Bri," Tacker said, watching the milk swirl and cloud in his cup.

"They bliddy fitches!" Midge squawked.

"At least they earns their keep," said Tacker.

Midge was ugly in a fat, slovenly sort of way. Her hair was short, dry and mousy and she had a disturbing habit of picking at her bad teeth with a fingernail. I was a bit afraid of her because she wasn't all there and had a terrible temper.

It was a relief to slip into the yard where the ferret hutch stood under an awning of timber and corrugated iron. I unlatched the wire-netting door and Ladyship came to me calmly. The other jill stretched and went back to sleep. Tacker lavished attention on them, feeding them rabbit in fur and birds in feather, entrails and chicken heads.

"Here 'er be, Billyboy," Tacker chuckled, and I put the jill on the table among the debris of last night's supper. She sat on her haunches and sniffed the warm kitchen odours.

"I wish Billy would eat the lil bastard," Midge said and the murder in her voice chilled me.

"Shut up, you mazed cow," said Tacker.

"You loves they fitches," Midge said. "You loves 'em but you don't love me."

Tacker drank his coffee and made no reply.

Thirty-five years passed before his idiosyncrasies and traits clicked sharply into focus again and the experiences we shared fell easily on to paper. Much of Tacker went towards the creation of the trapper, Leonard Scoble, in my novel *A Black Fox Running*. But the real man was neither good nor bad. He was coarse, cheerful, a little cruel and amoral, living according to his instincts. This classic human predator obeyed laws older by many millennia than the rules and codes of civilization – fox law, law of crow and wolf and eagle. He may have looked like a twentieth-century man but he belonged in spirit to pre-Roman Britain, to anarchy and immediacy.

Through Tacker I learnt about "fitches and fairs" – stoats and weasels, "drummers and fuzz-pigs" – rabbits and hedgehogs, "goyals and dawbakes" – little coombes on wild hillsides and scarecrows. Piece by piece the jigsaw of Yokel shintoism fell into place and Tacker continued to push back the frontiers of my childhood world. Once we followed a stream amid the quiet fall of pine cones and the rattle and swish of blackbirds, out of the trees into a vista of farmland rolling to breathtaking horizons. It was beyond Hallwell looking across the South Hams towards Start Point. Even Tacker was impressed although his mind was propping up the bar. The jill ferret made his trouser pocket quake.

"Bide still, ma boodie," he whispered.

We slithered down the pasture and the clean, mossy scent of rabbits wafted from the sack he was shouldering.

"Won't the ferret bite your willie?" I said.

"Ferrets doan eat willies, boy," he laughed. "Dap along smartish now. Us don't want to be this side of the river come night."

I was carrying the spade and the purse nets. When we came over the Dart we didn't bring snares and gins. It was too risky. Tacker had twelve convictions for poaching and theft, and creeping old age had made him abandon most of his swash-buckling enterprises like raiding the pheasant coops and netting mallard on Victoria Park pond.

The Morris van was parked under the oaks in the lane by the Gara River. Parry lowered the driver's window and flicked out his dog-end.

"Jesus, man," he whined. "I'm freezin'. You're an hour late. Midge will give you hell."

The frail, white-faced runt of a Welshman was a dole-queue regular and a hardened scrumpy-drinker. He had a tongue like poison ivy and the disposition of Tojo. On poaching expeditions nearer home Tacker preferred my company for I kept my mouth shut and obeyed orders.

"Parry's got too much yap," Tacker said. "But you're orright boy. You gets on with the job and says nort."

Going wild with Tacker was more exciting than sailing with Ulysses but the sight of a fox squirming in one of his heavy gins was hard to stomach. Sometimes I felt I had betrayed myself and that the game of childhood was forever being eclipsed by the grim adult world. Living close to the land had taught me about the ephemeral quality of Nature's beauty. Outside the wilder-ness places it was often flawed and Man was the imperfect ingredient, vomiting his inner-ugliness on landscapes and creatures. Winter morning of hoarfrost and the badger bucking in the snare. Blue sky and the gun-blasted pigeon tumbling from lovely, vivid life into darkness. Mist, dew and a singing sunrise, and the trapped rabbit pressed close to the ground waiting for death. Dear God, but there was so much killing going on around me – for sport, for the table, and I was born into it and schooled to its subtleties by those close to me.

Tacker had a slaughterhouse mentality and he shot count-less pheasants, pigeons, partridges, ducks, hawks and crows; rabbits, hares and foxes, stoats, weasels, squirrels and gone-wild cats. He dug and baited badgers, netted rabbits and hares, and hooked trout. Truly he was of the copses, fields and hedgerows as the barn owl was of the dump and Clennon's watermeadows, but he could not look and love what he saw and walk away uplifted. Death never had a busier henchmen, and he and the

ferrets had a lot in common. I have seen his face in Brueghel's
pictures – brutish, simple, ruddy, a face you would expect
to glimpse peeping into cattlepens or beaming at the doomed
Christmas fowls or leering at the pig being dragged off to saus-
agedom. He was the South Devon countryside and lived in it and
died in it.

So I had my red indian guide but whatever virtues lodged in
his soul I had bestowed from my imagination. Yet there are
memories of days and nights spent trapesing around with him
which have the glitter of childhood Christmasses. One such
occasion was a Saturday morning. Tacker had hidden the trapping gear by the pond at Berry Pomeroy and we had walked to
Stoke Gabriel for cider and pies at the Church House Inn. We
returned through Aish along a road barred with the shadows of
giant Scots pines; and the distance flickered as we trudged into
it. On the right at the crossroads was a garden full of evergreen
shrubs and under the eaves of the country house doves sat in
white silence. Then, from the remote reaches of a middle class
drawing room came the sound of a baritone singing something
fine, possibly one of Schubert's songs.

We cased the chicken farms and smallholdings and did a lot
of crawling through brambles before arriving at Berry Pomeroy
at sundown. Rabbits are most active early in the morning and
late in the evening. While the light faded I hammered home the
pegs and set the snares where the runs had been flattened by
over-use. Billy lay among the bare spokes of hemlock watching
me, his nose jerking up whenever woodpigeons hurtled by. Did
he see the freshness and sparkle of the landscape or enjoy the
repose a fine evening brings to the countryside? There was light
around us, curiously soft and vibrant, and a clarity of distance
that left me spellbound. I had seen animals standing quietly,
staring up at the sky, and I wondered if sheep, cows and horses
felt the beauty as I did.

The hilltop spinney where I had built my fire and pretended
to be Henry Williamson's crowstarver was a funny little clump
of dwarf oaks and taller beech trees. We flopped down in the
dead leaves and I heard the squeak of the cork being drawn from
Tacker's medicine bottle of scrumpy. The air was suddenly
spiced with the keen vinegary smell of cider. Tacker smacked his
lips and put a match to an own roll and the pheasants erupted
from the gloom behind us like a firework display. My fingertips

were crackling but Tacker puffed at his fag and swore softly to himself.

"I should have knowed," he lamented. "The crafty lil sods – I should've knowed."

Darkness silted the valley and lights hardened into brilliance. Then there was a loud fall of rooks and daws, succeeded by an enduring hush. South of Dartmoor Devon was the floor of some gigantic smithie, spark-dusted and seamed with red and gold. I could pick out individual towns and villages and indulge the sweet melancholy that visited me at such moments.

The cries of tawny owls rang through the coombes and woods, and a black shape dropped into the branches above me and hooted. Tacker sucked at his dog-end and touched Billy's ears.

"Us best get home, boy," he said. "Midge turns mean if I miss supper."

7
Jubilee Street Primary

The chickens were singing like banjos and the sun through the
haze was a goldfish in a frozen pond. I left for school early,
tugging the collar of my navy-blue gabardine up round my ears
against the cold and stopping every so often to rub some warmth
back into my bare knees. Jubilee Street Primary was a collection
of grey buildings assembled by a Victorian council that believed
a blend of ecclesiastical and almshouse styles encouraged an
appetite for learning and obedience in poor children. Here I
spent some of my happiest hours despite the Draconian rule of
the headmaster who over-subscribed to the maxim: spare the
rod and spoil the child. His code had been tailor-made to fit
those years of austerity when food rationing, the housing shortage, power cuts and rising prices made living a penance for most
grown-ups.

My personal problem was the difficulty I had in adjusting to
school discipline after months of the Romany life. But returning
to Jubilee Street Primary meant the chance to see the volupt-
uous Beryl Eccles flaunting her gym knickers during playground
PE and running around all flushed and seductive and naughty.
Those boys caught loitering hopefully in the girls' cloakroom
after PE were dragged before the headmaster and caned. Lust
was definitely discouraged at Jubilee Street where the spartan

regime pursued an odd brand of monastic athleticism popular with the Church of England, a sort of public school hand-down. Sex was considered the most heinous sin. To be apprehended tugging your toggle in the lavatory meant a caning before the entire school. And the boy and girl found playing mothers and fathers faced terrible consequences including a detailed account of the "perversion" being related to their parents.

". . . that's it, Mrs X – both he and the girl were – er – ah unclothed from the – er – waist downwards, fiddling with each other's – er – um – private parts."

I escaped this excruciating embarrassment by a hair's breadth.

In the main playground – a patch of concrete not much larger than a tennis court – stood an air-raid shelter. Here three of us hornier lads enticed Beryl Eccles and her wanton and equally big friend, Doreen Harris, to do rude things. Choking with excitement and the front of our shorts poking out like clowns' hats we watched the girls strip off and go through the "nurse-examine-you" routine. Then this little toad, Clarke Herbert, stuck his head round the door and yelled: "You're being dirty, all of you, and I'm telling."

While the others stood there transfixed I nipped outside and cornered Clarke by the drinking fountain. He had been named after Clark Gable and his sole claim to fame was a facility for peeing twice his own height against the urinal wall.

"I saw you, Carter."

"Where to, Clarke? I mean – I've been all over the place."

"In the shelter. Them girls had their knickers down."

"I wasn't there, Clarke – honest, God's honour. I was up the lav with Butch Meredith and –"

"Well, it looked like you," he said slowly, doubt clouding his eyes.

I wanted to kick him but instead I gave him the slice of cold toast I'd brought for lunch and some of Hopkins's home-made humbugs. The toad munched and smiled and crossed me off his hit-list. But the other nymphs and satyrs refused to take him seriously and after prayers the next morning they were publicly denounced and led to the headmaster's study for big doses of bamboo.

In a sense Mr Greensleeves, the head, was a pioneer of the feminist movement. He believed in beating both girls and boys for the most trivial of offences such was his zeal for equality of the sexes. Talking after the whistle had been blown to signify the end of the playtime meant a vigorous caning. Talking before or during or after his special lessons was suicidal. And if anyone left a scrap of school dinner uneaten his bamboo would sing its disapproval.

Egon Ronay would not have approved of those culinary outrages we were expected to scoff, and many a child was forced to sit miserably all afternoon contemplating cold congealed fatty meat and the burnt roast beetroot and the burnt gravy the dinner ladies had shovelled onto his plate. Refusing to join the school dining club I tucked whole helpings of poison veg behind the radiators and changed places regularly to avoid detection.

Fortunately Mr Greensleeves only stormed into our lives occasionally and was content to administer small doses of violence to remind us of the ultimate authority. On that cold January morning the playground was crowded with noisy, happy children – little Lowry figures modelling utility clothes. It was a grey, navy-blue and brown scene; grey balaclavas, navy-blue macs, brown and grey coats, grey socks and stockings, grey short trousers and skirts, grey pullovers and grey skirts. But our cheeks were red and so were the girls' lips, and blonde pigtails, sunkissed and dancing, were heaven to behold. We played "he" and tennis ball soccer, and cowboys and indians. Often there were piggyback battles before the assembly bell rang and we crocodiled through the cloakroom depositing topcoats and head-gear en route to the hall via the classroom and the register check.

Colin Yeo, Butch Meredith and I found the march tune which swept us into assembly slightly insane. Dink dink-a-dink dink, dinka dinka, dink, dinka dink dink dink dink dink a dink. Miss Preece belted it out on the piano and we reacted like hysterical puppets, keeping a wary eye on Greensleeves who had mounted his rostrum to conduct the proceedings with his best cane.

"All things bright and beautiful, all creatures great and small", we sang from the heart. Then:

> Bring me my bow of burning gold
> Bring me my arrows of dee – zyurr;
> Bring me my spear o clouds unfold
> Bring me my chariot of vi – yurr.

And singing I looked up and saw the bridge of fire between myself and the winter sun arching out of the window. "Lovely Jesus," I prayed, "look after Nibs. She idn well and I don't want her to die. I know she's just a cat but I love her. Will she go to heaven when she dies? I don't want to go up there if her idn waiting for me." I was all out of breath and close to yelling. But Mr Greensleeves thought it improper to encourage deep emotion in boys and girls and the swish of his cane suppressed all spontaneity. The art class was an example of his eagerness to clip adventurous wings. He drew geometric patterns on the blackboard and we had to copy them. So the gut feeling I had for shape and colour was never really liberated until I got to Torquay Grammar School.

"What's Time, Mam?" I asked.

"It's the clock, Bri. Tick-tock – up there on the mantelpiece."

"But we were talking about cavemen today. They didn't have clocks."

"But they had Time. There's always been Time. It's autumn and spring. It's part of things."

I wasn't convinced, possibly because I had an unconscious desire to escape mechanical time. I saw the caveman standing on Hay Tor, reading the air with his nose like a fox. Those primitive men were strong in animal ways, like Tacker, but lacked Tacker's worldliness. They never ran ahead of the moment and their gods were kind, horned and taloned, winged or simply trees. The Christian God of Mr Greensleeves was on the side of the glum and the staid. Watching the stern, unbending headmaster conducting the hymn-singing I recalled his tolling voice breathing fire into the incantation of the multiplication tables.

The rain was soaking my hair, laying dark aprons on the playground. I stared through the shower out of the gateway at the little spikey trees and the knots of headscarved mothers waiting for the four o'clock bell. Presently I was turning into Fisher Street and running past the old farm buildings and Miss Hannaford's corner shop. A nun hurried by praying to herself. Then a tweedy woman exercising a couple of labradors. She had an uncreased, full face and it smiled at me and spouted pleasantries in a plummy voice when I crumpled the dogs' ears.

Rain hammered down and powdered away. A car sizzled out of the ruined charcoal sketch of distance and chugged on up the hill. Dimpsey settled quickly on such afternoons and soon Butch and Colin were shinning up the lamp posts to turn things on for the lamplighter. Tacker and Parry paused by the convent school gates and kicked the mud off their boots. The rabbits hanging from bits of cord attached to their belts bounced limply. They had been reduced to mere things with dull eyes and black crumbs of blood clotting the fur around their mouths.

Tacker grinned at me, thinking I was envying him his freedom. But he was wrong. School was another sort of adventure and Miss Lee, the teacher we all loved, could cast a net of wisdom and catch little butterflies of truth for us to examine and understand. She taught us about the spiritual pilgrimage that begins at birth. People see truths, have visions and convert others. Most important she offered moral compass bearings and taught me that even if we stray from truth we can always return to it, no matter how late. In the hall on wet afternoons she let us sample classical music on gramophone records. It was what I craved for. I would hear snatches of symphonies and concertos at the cinema or catch a few bars of something magical from the windows of big houses. But Miss Lee brought into my life the sad day's end glow of Elgar's music, and I sat cross-legged on the floor under the spell of sound sculpted into cloud and hill, field, wood and market town. I carried it with me to Clennon. Chanson du matin swept me up Cider Mill Hill to the great sunbright place. But as I climbed the cloud shadows drowned the singing ecstasy of light and the whole of South Devon melted into something more mysterious than haze. England was my spiritual possession and I was aware of the biblical presence of the valley where the sweet familiar places ascended out of daybreak to glitter in a freshening breeze. Gulls flashed across the stark hedges and a cold silence presided over the empty birds' nests. Clennon was the estuary of all my emotions and I came there stripped of civilization's gloss.

*   *   *

Miss Preece was small, skinny, flat-chested, elderly, bespectacled, and humourless. She looked like a cross between Old Mother Riley and Popeye's Olive Oil. Miss Gilcrest was young, creamy-skinned, plump and sexy in the style of Snow White. But Miss Lee was the earth mother of Jubilee Street. She was homely, beautifully ugly and dumpy with the smile of God's favourite angel. From her we learnt the folk dances of many countries and there was a goodness in her that was radiant. We would sit enthralled while she spoke, guiding us over foreign hills or leading us image by image up country lanes.

Ours was quite a remarkable class. Half were destined for Grammar School but we all shared a strong pastoral instinct and knew the names of the common wild flowers and birds. We were very fortunate to be young at that time, living in the twilight of a greener more leisurely age. Even the smoking chimneys which created the smogs of the Fifties brought romance to the back-streets at dusk and filled me with yearning for something I could not unravel — Avalon perhaps.

Greensleeves's collection of bamboos failed to banish the dreams which visited me at my desk and Miss Lee milked these dreamscapes and helped me turn them into pictures and stories. She encouraged me to draw and write, and it soon became apparent that my pictures had unusual elements of design and perspective. Mr Greensleeves was not impressed and kept me drawing patterns with ruler and compass, and criticized my use of colour schemes like purple, brown and dark green. Yet his emphasis on discipline sank in and was the perfect foundation for academic progress. Alas, though, his lessons were grim and serious and robbed the class of its aura of joy that is so precious and fleeting. The tense atmosphere of these lectures defied interruption but there were occasions when comedy entered uninvited like a virus in a maternity ward.

We sang the old hymns with gusto and danced and skipped about to the school percussion "ensemble". Close to the surface ribald, irreverent and defiant forces flickered. Sometimes a dozen boys linked arms and marched about the playground singing "Old soldiers never die, they only fade away". Demonstrations of this nature set the seal on comradeship and strengthened the warrior bond. It seemed important to learn the scurrilous words of Colonel Bogey and bawl them at lah-di-dah girls of Sonia Johnsie's ilk whose dads managed greengrocers' shops or were solicitors' clerks.

> Hitler has only got one ball,
> Goering has two but one too small;
> Himmler has something sim'lar
> But poor old Goebbels has no balls at all.

The poor German was still public enemy number one whether he was a nazi or not. Now the bombing was over and the threat of invasion had vanished for good we could crow and strut and show the flag. The grey buildings and drab little playground had no ill-effects. Who, after all, is an aesthete at nine years old? What Jubilee Street lacked in spaciousness and light it made up in cosiness and the certainty of belonging.

Nine-year-olds were considered capable of making and playing wooden recorders. Mr Greensleeves taught us to read simple melodies like "J'ai un bon tabac" and anyone caught blowing a wrong note was hauled out and whacked. Therefore, tone-deaf kids worked hard at conning the headmaster – much to the amusement of the rest of us. But one bitter January afternoon a boy named Harry Burridge fell victim of his own ingenuity and Mr Greensleeves's stoatlike ability for sniffing out lame rabbits.

Burridge had the IQ of a sheep and in customary fashion went astray during the performance of "Jesu Joy of Man's Desiring". Desperately trying to cover his blunder the imbecile performed without actually blowing into his instrument. But Mr Greensleeves knew. He had heard enough weird tootlings to put him on edge and was prowling about trying to bolt the culprits. He came and listened to us, individually. His body odour held the peculiar unpleasantness of dog excrement, faint yet recognisable in warm rooms, and it accentuated his menace. When he reached Burridge the boy began to tremble and the headmaster pounced crying "Ha-ha, Burridge! Enjoying yourself?" The distraught pseudo-musician smiled moronically, recorder still wedged in his mouth and his finger twitching on the holes.

"I can't hear anything, Burridge," roared Mr Greensleeves. "Go to my office and I'll see if I can get some sort of sound out of you."

"Go to my office" was the Jubilee Street death sentence and I had enough bamboo during my last years at primary school to keep my hands and bum permanently aglow.

"What did you do today, Bri?" Mam said, easing the pasties out of the oven.

I sat at the kitchen table and pinched the bits of dough she had left for me.

"Music was funny. Harry Burridge got the cane for not playing proper."

"That'll teach him," Mam said softly as she slid the pasties back into the oven.

The window was steamed over and outside the stag wind of winter was driving into the corners of the yard.

"It's going to snow," Mam added. And I could see the mountains of some unnamed place where whiteness purred down the gulleys. And my hands enfolded the big mug of tea and I blew into it, making a dimple in the glossy, brown surface.

8
The Big, Big Wave

The rabbits fed delicately, munching the hard green cabbage leaves and half mouldy carrots. I lingered by the hutch and stroked Nibs and made little mewing noises like a blade of grass being drawn between thumb and forefinger.

"The pigeons have gone, Bri," Dad said. His hands were sunk deep in the pockets of his overalls and he stared uncomfortably down at the ground. I waited for him to explain.

"A cat got them. Mrs Burnett says it was that bloody Doodlebug. She saw him from her bedroom window."

"Three pigeons!" I exclaimed. "Doodlebug got all three?"

"I know. It's daft but there you are."

I began to shiver and he laid a hand on my shoulder.

"It's cold," I said, gathering up Nibs and holding her close.

"Here's two bob," Dad mumbled. "Go and get yourself a bottle of fizz and some chips. And there's a surprise inside the house."

"What is it, Dad?"

"Wait till you come back from the chip shop."

I ran up the wet street, dodging the bicycles of the home-coming workers and reached Evans's chippie as the door opened.

"What's the hurry?" asked Mrs Evans and she shot scribbles – little bits of fried batter – onto the chips which lay steaming inside a small dunce's cap of newspaper.

"Dad fell through the roof of the house he's building."

"Get home! Is he orright?"

"Lost both legs," I said.

"Then he had the artificial ones fitted bloody quick," Mr Evans said appearing at the side door with a tray of fish pieces. "I saw Perce down Penks fifteen minutes ago, you lying little sod."

The chips were crisp and hot and the scribbles dark and crunchy. I walked quickly back to the terrace stuffing handfuls into my face, the bottle of Corona's Dandelion and Burdock tucked under my arm. Then I was pushing open the living room door and grinning happily at our first wireless.

"Don't you dare touch it," Mam said. "I'm the only one who knows how to work it."

"It" was big and cream and heavy looking. She switched it on and fumbled the tuning knob.

"Get me some music, Mam," I cried and she did – the big band sound of a palais de dance orchestra swinging through "The Woodchoppers' Ball".

"Bloody noise," Dad said.

"Can't you get any proper music, Mam?"

She glared at me and switched off the wireless and said:

"It goes on when I say so. I paid for it with my Co-op divi. It's mine."

Dad shook his head and smiled sadly.

"You won't want to go the pictures tomorrow night, then?" he said.

"What's on?" said Mam, running a duster over her new toy.

"*Holiday in Mexico*, at the Regent."

"Who's in it?"

"Walter Pidgeon and Jane Powell."

"Well," she muttered and drew a deep breath. "Well, we'll see."

*   *   *

We did most of our shopping in Winner Street and around Foale's Corner but when Mam couldn't get into town I had to run down to Hannaford's or go up to St Michael's, risking injury from members of rival street gangs. About that time we received our allocation of Spanish oranges – a pound for every ration-book holder, and Mam made sure I had the lot.

"The poor little bugger needs building up," she said and Dad agreed.

As soon as she started thumbing through the ration books I knew it wouldn't be long before I was running an errand.

"Go down Hannaford's, Bri, and get me some flour and half a pound of marge. Quick now or your Dad will be home before his tea's ready."

Hannaford's was a seedy little corner shop run by a fat woman who had a teenage daughter but no husband yet managed to display the "respectable" label in the most demanding and hypocritical of societies.

Before the doorbell stopped tinkling behind me Mrs Hannaford sailed out of the parlour in all her unsmiling majesty. As she lifted the curtain that separated shop from backroom I glimpsed her infirm budgie in his cage and her bloomers airing on the fireguard.

Tacking between the tins and boxes she arrived breathless at the counter and glared down at me from the massive overhang of her bosom. In her opinion boys were congenital criminals and I was high on a list of suspects headed by Horseshit O'Flaherty. So all she kept on the counter was an enuretic tom cat called Peter and a bag of dried peas which the mice used as a lavatory. Neither Mrs Hannaford nor Piddly Pete ever caught a mouse. The shop was small and dark and doomed to extinction long before the other corner shops vanished in the shadow of the supermarkets. And it was littered with unsprung mousetraps. You could hear the impudent little pilferers scampering about behind the biscuit tins and crates while Pete dozed and piddled his neutered life away. Everything bought at Hannaford's smelt of cat, and a fuzz of his hairs clung to the treacle toffee. During the years of Piddly Pete's tenancy of the counter I must have consumed pounds of his discarded grey fur.

*   *   *

The big shopping was done at the Co-op which was a sombre temple of working-class commerce pickled in Edwardianism. Here the underpaid nosed out bargains and the assistants squandered civility on nasty old ladies and mothers beseiged by raucous brats. Cheese was cut and weighed; bacon was sliced; and pounds, shillings and pence whizzed overhead in little cups on wires.

The place fascinated me for the wrong reasons. Those constantly smiling men, busying over Mam's order, weren't like the rough mates Dad brought home to supper after chucking-out time on Saturday nights. The Co-op misters were pink and spruce with clean nails. They spoke a bland over-the-counter jargon, dispensing information liberally sprinkled with clichés and platitudes. But they were polite and considerate in an age of politeness and consideration.

We street arabs bowed to no one and led by the fearless O'Flaherty gave all shop assistants a hard time. It is a pity we lose the sharp inner-eye of childhood, for very few sacred cows would survive if adults possessed the vision of nine-year-olds. Going to the Co-op in a chirping gang meant an orgy of mischief and the manager would follow us around wearing an expression of neurotic despair. Assistants snarled: "Stop handling the goods. Leave those apples alone. Get that dog outside." But impertinent, grubby little fingers continued to poke the cheese and black fingernails scored the virginal bars of Lifebuoy and carbolic soap; and snotty noses lingered hopefully, hoovering up the fragrance of coffee beans and spices.

Shoplifting, despite the temptation and opportunity, was rare. Although we capered to the Devil's tune we carried memories of Eden in our souls. Maybe the "Pray or Burn" warning on the Salvation Army banner helped but I doubt it. Nearly every family I knew courted respectability. The clean windows and laundered curtains and scrubbed steps advertised self-respect and pride. And I was never allowed to go to school in dirty shoes or with a hole in my sock. What the neighbours thought carried more weight than the threat of eternal damnation and the fires of hell.

*   *   *

"England lost the Ashes, Dad. It was on the news."

"Good," Dad grunted, smoothing the fatigue out of his face with work-worn hands. "Bloody cricket. It's almost as daft as bloody golf. All those grown men chasing a little ball. Christ! I'd love to go on strike like the lorry drivers. Bloody hard graft is no use to anyone."

"They're still shooting our policemen out in Palestine," Mam said, placing his tripe and onions before him and getting busy with the breadknife. She had a brother-in-law in the Palestine police and felt it her duty to keep an eye on the activities of the Jewish terrorists – Irgun Zvai Leumi.

"Nearly seven years of bombing and shooting, shit and misery and they still carry on," Dad said. "And Stalin's turned nasty after all we did for him."

"But we got the atom bomb," said Mam.

He nodded and forked the steaming white rubbery mess into his mouth and frowned at me and said:

"Want to go to the pictures with your Mam and me next Saturday afternoon?"

"We're going to the Picture House to see Robert Donat in *The Citadel*," Mam said.

"And Monte Hale in *Man from Rainbow Valley*."

"Me and Butch are thinking of watching Paignton Town," I said. "They're playing Brixham Rovers Reserves at home."

"It'll be bloody cold down on the green with this east wind blowing," Dad said.

"I'm glad he's not ferreting around with Tacker every spare minute of the day," said Mam.

"Tacker's ill," I said. "He's got bronchitis."

"You had that bad when you were a baby," Mam sighed.

"Tell me about it, Mam."

"Yes," said Dad grinning, "I could use another helping of tripe."

The wireless wasn't fascinating enough to keep me in of an evening. After tea the kids gathered by the Marist Convent gates to play rough games of roller-skate hockey with walking sticks and a tennis ball; or street soccer, up to twenty a side and all hell let loose for the people who lived between Mumford's yard and Eden Place.

Desperate to preserve his shop windows Mr Penk talked Colin Yeo into persuading us to join the cubs. I think it was the mention of camping holidays on Dartmoor that pushed us towards the Parish Church Hall, curious to find out what excited those green-jerseyed, green-capped kids. We dibbed and dobbed and tried to take the portly Archela seriously until O'Flaherty set fire to the wastepaper basket and encouraged us to dance around it like the Black Feet in a recent Bug House offering of Gene Autrey. Horseshit regretted our mass expulsion because he had heard Bob-a-Job Week could be really lucrative. Our attempts to infiltrate other cub packs failed but we weren't too concerned.

Ever questing for adventure we gathered on Paignton seafront to stare at the surf and lean at an angle of forty-five degrees into the storm force easterly. Aurora Penk, the newsagent's ten-year-old daughter, had started following me about making calf-eyes. Her eyes were green and her smile dazzling but the gang were not keen to have her tagging along and I was reluctant to show any interest despite a swelling of the heart whenever she approached.

Butch Meredith also fell under her spell and we competed for her attention by showing off in the most reckless and flamboyant fashion. The big dare was the Prom Dash from the harbour end of the seafront, on the unprotected seaward side of the wall, up to the iron railings opposite the site of the summer bandstand. Even a moderately rough sea on a high tide made this a perilous run. The waves swept unimpeded over the promenade before rushing back again. Stray dogs were sometimes caught and sucked out to a watery grave.

At the end of January the seas were monstrous, exploding in peacock-tinted fans against the end of the pier and the harbour wall. But separating each roller was a long interval of choppy turbulence and a boy moving quickly had a slight chance of covering the distance safely. If a wave surprised us it wouldn't be difficult to climb the wall and drop down behind it for nothing worse than a drenching. Butch and I were old hands at this game but we had never seen such mean white water.

O'Flaherty, who could not swim and hated the sea, eyed us with something close to respect as he organized the spectators on top of the wall, half-way along the Dash.

"They oughtn't to do it," Aurora said. "They'll get drowned."

"No they won't," Colin Yeo said. "Anyrate they can swim."

"Not in them waves," said Soapy Tucker. "I'm goin' to get a policeman."

"You do and you'll get this," O'Flaherty growled, lifting a fist; but for once Soapy followed his instincts and headed for town.

"Not yet," Butch cried above the roar of the surf. "Wait a minute, Bri. Let's wait a minute."

"You're shit scared," I sneered and was off, keeping a beady eye on the sea.

The last wave to break had left a sheet of foam on the promenade. Spindrift bounced and sailed across the shallows like tumbleweed. The wind screamed in my ears and punched me off balance and I accidentally shoulder-charged Butch. We staggered and giggled and ran on. Out beyond the pier a great black wall of water stood up and rolled towards the shore. Butch glanced at me, his mouth gaping from a white little face, but some demon drove me past the amazed gang who were shouting now and pointing. The railings were fifty yards away.

The black wall curled and almost collapsed and Butch and I were fooled. We expected the wave to disintegrate and shoot up the beach, white and low. But it didn't. It merely stumbled and lurched and gathered momentum to hit the shallows and crumple with a kind of muscular surge. The thunder made me turn and claw at the wall. Luckily I found a good foothold and sprang up and somersaulted over onto the road. Moments later the sea arched white above me and boiled around me and I was swilling about underwater among the ornamental gardens at the bottom of Torbay Road. I came to rest against the rockery and sat there spitting and coughing.

"Where's Butch?" Colin bawled. The others joined me and stood, arms away from their bodies soaked to the skin and paler than pout whitings.

"Butch," sobbed Barry Salter.

I shook my head and a policeman, some council gardeners and Soapy Tucker splashed up to us.

"Butch is still in the sea," Aurora screamed.

"O Christ!" one of the men said. "How did it happen?"

"That doesn't matter," said the policeman. "Stay here and I'll have a look."

"Butch. Butch," Soapy cried. "It's your fault, Carter. You dared him."

The policeman was crouching and running for the sea wall. Then he suddenly swerved away and we saw what had caught his attention and we ran after him, the fear falling from our limbs. Butch Meredith was wading through the flood-water down on the green looking wan and shocked and half dead. Later we learnt how he had sprinted on and actually reached the railings only to be blasted under them and onto the town football pitch by the wave.

"It was twenty feet high," he lied. "Bloody hell! – thought I was a gonner. But I made it, Bri. I got to the railings and you didn't."

"Like a headless chicken," O'Flaherty said knowingly.

"Your mum'll kill you, Butch," Aurora said. "Your clothes are ruined."

"Stay away from the sea – all of you," the policeman said, "or you'll be wearing shrouds."

For the rest of the week Butch was a playground hero and every kid in Jubilee Street Primary wanted to hear him tell the story of his miraculous escape from death. The wave got higher and higher in the telling until Sonia Johnsie worked out that if it really had been so huge it would have flattened everything right up to Foale's Corner. O'Flaherty, who was a Roman Catholic and went to the Catholic School, gave his own version to his classmates, claiming it was he who had ridden the wave up to Torbay Road right into Victoria Street as far as Foale's the butcher. While he strutted and bragged Butch pretended to be modest and let people coax the story out of him with the help of sweets and primary school treasure like marbles, cigarette cards and lead soldiers.

But Aurora was not seduced by the glory Butch reaped from his moment of blind panic. She shared her beef-and-mustard sandwiches with me during morning playtime and gave me bits of chocolate she filched from her Dad's shop. Then the blizzard arrived and I caught ringworm and Aurora and everyone else were forbidden to come near me.

9
Ghost in the Copse

Emerging from sleep I was aware of a far-off prolonged howling. Poking my head out from under the eiderdown I saw a white glow framed by the window and knew instantly what it signified. An amazing sight was waiting for me as I wiped away the condensation and peered out. Elmsleigh Road was a river of drifting snow and flakes like white tracer bullets sped from blackness into the street lights. Snow smoked and fumed and fretted, and I could see the treetops bending in Mr Mortimer's garden at the bottom of the terrace and feel the cold pushing through the glass into my nose which was pressed against the window. O God, I prayed, don't let it stop. Let it fall for a week and please make it settle. If I hadn't been shivering so much I wouldn't have gone back to bed but it was the warmest place and I was still drowsy despite the excitement.

Next morning there was a white light on the ceiling and outside random flakes fell from a grey sky into a white hush. Dad remained happily in bed and Mam cursed the weather both he and I loved for different reasons. While I ate my porridge she stared out at the drifts and sucked her breath through her teeth and said:

"The wind's coming off the sea again. There's more snow on the way. Damned horrible stuff. Damned winter."

I grinned gleefully at Nibs. Mam preferred her snow in the Mabinogion or *Pickwick Papers* but snow in the town meant trouble and hard work.

"I can't get the back door open," she grunted. Then she raised her voice so that Dad would hear.

"Perhaps Lord Muck will heave his carcass off the mattress before dinner time and give us a hand."

"I'm asleep," Dad said. "Send for the council. Make those idle buggers earn their wages."

I pulled on my wellingtons and buttoned my mac over my corduroy lumber jacket, and Mam straightened my balaclava.

"Don't you go far," she said. "And keep that scarf across your chest or you'll be coughing phlegm."

I crammed the cheese and chutney sandwiches and three jam tarts in Dad's old fishing bag and cautiously opened the front door. The wind had risen again and was sculpting the drifts. I had never seen so much snow.

"Brian," Mam called.

"I'm only going to Gran's," I lied and ploughed up the terrace in case she changed her mind and decided to keep me in by the fire.

Beyond the deserted streets the savage north easterly was lifting the surface powder and whisking it away in white clouds and columns. A coppery glow lit the sky just above the sea and the sound of heavy surf carried inland to magnify the sense of desolation. Snow fell from the wind-scurry, lovely whiteness to cancel out civilization; and mallard came low and untidy in the teeth of the blizzard, each flight unsure and noisy. But above the shriek of the wind I heard the music of high-flying geese and saw the dark lines of birds lifting and falling. A desire for some unravished, unknown place made me hold my breath and wish. A blast of snow sent me reeling. The marshes and water-meadows were alive with wildfowl and the double clap of a twelve-bore filled the air with wings. Tacker was at work, visiting the traps he had set in the mud for ducks. He shot oystercatchers, curlew and herons that winter and left them lifeless for the scavengers to pick clean. His path to hell was littered with murdered creatures. But two selves were warring in my own body – one the hunter who could gather a shot mallard from the reeds and see only the carcass glazed with honey lying in state among the roast potatoes, peas and carrots;

the other, the novice priest who worshipped nature and ran on
the high octane fuel of idealism and romance. Later I would
experience a blinding moment of revelation on my personal
Road to Damascus and never kill a creature again.

All day I wandered through the valley and the woods, seek-
ing out the deepest drifts, skidding across the solid ponds and
drainage guts. I was at the centre of a whining gloom and
sometimes I felt curiously dazed and weightless, and thought the
winter was trying to tell me something. Or maybe those pure
animal men who had lived here before history had spoken the
language of the wind and the trees, and had left the deathless
part of themselves in the field corners and on the hilltops.

From such mysteries I plodded on to the agonizing beauty of
sunset and found a dead pigeon by Broome Linhay. It had been
shot and had fallen beyond the nose of the sportsman's dog.

The sky cleared a little at dimpsey and revealed the moon in
its last quarter. Rabbits pushed their way out of the blocked
warrens and stared across the whiteness. Against the hedges the
poor, miserable sheep steamed and bleated. They were always
left out in rough weather but the cattle were brought indoors. I
tried not to disturb them as I approached the potato clamp and
excavated enough Red Soils for the Sunday meal. And quite
suddenly I was tired and hungry. I had walked in a great circle
past Cider Mill Farm, up over the fields to Windy Corner and
back to Cider Mill Hill, New Road Forest and Broome Linhay.
Between two reefs of cloud was the star-spangled way. Then it
vanished and the wind cut as cruelly as it sang, and I walked the
white road past the black houses under the black clouds. The
front of my coat was a sheet of ice and my balaclava had frozen
to my ears.

"Look at the state of you," Mam cried. "D'you think I've
nothing better to do than wash your clothes? Get in by the fire
and I'll heat some water for your bath."

But she was glad to see me and recounted in detail the
minutiae of her day. Thawing out at the fireside in vest and
pants I listened to the end of Children's Hour and the crackle of
frying kippers.

*   *   *

February proved a bad month for everyone except the children.
A new bogeyman had succeeded Hitler and we were all learning

to hate and fear Stalin. Meanwhile the sea froze at Folkestone and the German POW's were out with the troops trying to clear the roads and railways. The bread shortage and coal shortage coming on the heels of all the strikes helped to create an England most definitely unfit for heroes. There was a lack of moral stamina and Dad insisted the years of suffering had drained the nation of its willpower.

"We should never have got rid of Churchill," he said. But the adult world barely ruffled my consciousness.

Standing by the Marist Convent gates miserably contemplating the thaw and hoping for a glimpse of Aurora I saw the young men paddling through the slush on their way to the Deller's Cafe dance. They looked like FBI agents from those really bad Hollywood gangster films – slouch hats, belted raincoats, suits tailored by monkeys with sheep shears, American cigarettes and a veneer of backstreet toughness. Then a long spell of arctic weather brought fresh snowfalls and Dad built me a toboggan that carried me down Cider Mill Hill at terrific speed. Occasionally Butch and Colin mitched from school and joined me at Clennon but usually I was alone and liked it that way.

Soon the toboggan was cast aside because it restricted my exploration and was difficult to hump over field walls and hedges. Sunrise among the milky hills meant blue shadows on the snow and the twinkle of hedgerow ice. Woodcock rattled up from their seats and whirred off low and fast. I crept up to the hedge and crouched there under the smoke of my breath. Winter had stripped the bank and its shrubs and plants down to the elementals. The brambles had become coils of barbed wire flung over brown jags, spikes and sticks. But in the lee, where the creepers of old man's beard were thick enough to be cut into lengths and smoked, lay a crust of fallen leaves. Here the robins, wrens, sparrows and Nordic thrushes scratched for insects, and that great opportunist feeder, the fox, came grubbing for beetles, woodmice and voles.

Small birds sat silently among the twigs and I scuffed around and uncovered the broken shell of a crow's egg, the mummified body of a starling and an old, rusty wristwatch. Pheasants had been turning over the debris under the dead bracken and the tracks of a pair of mated partridges snaked away from the hedge and converged in the centre of the field.

Snow made it possible for me to read the countryside partly from my own experience and partly from what I had learnt from Mam, Dad and Tacker. Where the field steepened I found the tracks of a brown hare, and close to the hedge were the delicate hieroglyphics of voles, mice and small birds, and the oval spoor of a walking fox. There were also less obvious clues to busy wildlife. Tacker had showed me how to locate little rodents. He had dug into the hedgerow earth and uncovered voles and mice which were eating the roots of a hazel. Ladyship the ferret relished a feed of woodmice.

The best lessons came from Nature itself, providing I was prepared to sit and watch and listen. A pine cone gnawed to the stump betrayed the presence of squirrels, for mice and other small creatures left far more of the cone because they had tiny teeth. A squirrel, too, would crack a hazelnut shell neatly in half and quarry into the kernel. But neither mice nor squirrels had savaged the few remaining rose hips. Finches had chipped away with their beaks to gobble up the berry pap.

I also got to know animals and birds by their droppings – the buzzards and owls by their mutes and pellets; the rabbit by its dry, fibrous buckshot; the twisted root of a fox's scat deposited near its scent post; the hard black marbles of a hare. Once I had learnt the alphabet the literature of the wild places made good reading.

*   *   *

Snow continued to fall as it did in the carol, snow on snow with little respite and little hope for the first crop of lambs. The glorious adventure of Clennon registered in a dreamlike, jigsaw way. The wind that brought the arctic to Devon rarely abated. It fashioned a blurred sonic world of vibrating skylines and a murk that swept out of the north east to unleash its cargo of white stair rods. I lifted my balaclava and the noise pounded my ears. Then the white-out passed and there were confrontations with trees and a blundering into waist-deep drifts.

Windless days possessed the eerie calm of cemeteries on grey November evenings. Stiff-faced and out of breath I'd stand among the waffling flakes hypnotized by the dizzy white scribbling and the silence. The solitude at such times was a little frightening. But the mood was fleeting and bird shapes would quake in the sky and brightness would flood the valley. Light would pour from a chasm in the clouds, clotted with daws and gulls and screeching starlings.

Such a day as this brought me to Lime Kiln Copse in search of pine cones for our fire. It was late afternoon and the dog star glinted on the frozen watermeadows down below the linhay. I crept through the scrub elm and sat with my back to a tree and yanked off a boot to pick the tiny balls of ice off my sock. A weird clacking sound close by made me jerk up my head and what I saw goose-pimpled me from nose to feet. Crouching in the lower branches of a crab apple tree was a ghost, whiter than snow and uglier than a monkey. Fear prevented me from crying out but the front of my trousers was suddenly very warm and wet. Then the 'ghost' quibbled its mandibles again and I saw the hooked beak and lidded eyes of a snowy owl. It had strayed far from its northern hunting grounds but the bird books described it as a rare winter vagrant.

Fear gave way to excitement. Everything had been orchestrated to make the bird seem huge – the bad light, my own smallness, its two-feet tall, fluffed-out full white shape barred and speckled with dark brown perched just above me. Those glittering black talons were capable of squeezing the life out of a rabbit and uneasiness crept once more through my curiosity. We gazed at each other and the owl seemed to delight in the way I quailed. Those lidded eyes alarmed and annoyed me and brought to mind portraits of haughty war leaders and politicians – men like Wellington at Waterloo, Napoleon at Borodino, and Lord Curzon of India. When I got up it fidgeted and clacked its fierce-looking mandibles and I thought it was going to attack me. So I bolted out into the dusk and ran home to bubble-and-squeak and piccalilli.

"There was this giant white owl in the copse, Dad," I said. "It was bigger than Gran."

"What did it do – peck out your brains?"

"It was a snowy owl from Lapland."

"If it's got any sense it'll fly back there," he said. "By Christ it was cold on that site this morning. Brass monkey weather."

"Have you ever seen a snowy owl, Dad?"

"No. Have you ever seen the oozy-oozy bird?"

"Perce," Mam said menacingly. "He's not one of your pub cronies."

"What's an oozy-oozy bird, Dad?"

"It's most odd. You see, it flies round and round in ever decreasing circles till it vanishes up its own –"

"Perce!" Mam grated through clenched teeth.

"– earhole," Dad grinned. "Anyway," he added. "Tell us about this giant owl."

The following day it was blowing a gale and the copse was tugging at its moorings, threatening to break loose and fly away. The snowy owl was gone and I did not see it again although I found a dead rabbit on the edge of New Road Forest, freshly gutted by a hooked upper mandible.

"I reckon its the beginning of a new ice age," Ernie said.

I had come to the end of the owl story and was jigging up and down in the farmyard trying to bring some life back into my toes.

"Struggling to carry off a sheep was it? Crikey, lad, it must have been some bird."

And he winked at me and I blushed.

"God's honour, Ernie," I said. "It was the size of – of Bath-sheba and had a beak like a five-ton grass hook."

"Us best get the rozzers and the army in, then," said Tony. The snot had frozen round his nostrils and his mouth was about as attractive as a fowl's behind.

"Your conk's all bunged up," I said, tapping the side of my nose with a forefinger.

Ernie laughed and ushered me into the stable out of harm's way. The lamp was lit and the horses were watered and I carried their feed from the cornbin in the cribs while Ernie mucked out. The animals' majesty touched me like a benediction. They were so gentle. I could imagine God feeling warm and drowsy and creating shire horses to adorn the first dimpsey of Eden. They chomped and munched and released great golden jets of urine which Tony always commented on but Ernie never seemed to notice.

The animals' beauty accompanied me into the morning.

"A real winter, boy," Mrs Brinham said, staring morosely at the frozen tap in Oppy Meadow just over the road from her cottage.

"He gave us a tap near home," she added. "But the thing's froze."

It was Oppy Meadow because it lay opposite Mill Marsh

Cottage. There was a splendid logic in many a country name even if a syllable or two was hacked off for convenience.

"You been round they old 'orses again? You'm 'orse mazed."

A shotgun banged down by Pucksbog.

"Tacker," I said sheepishly.

"Crool bugger, yaas," said Mrs Brinham. "Dad found some of his iron in the marsh. He tills gins for duck and catches all sorts. Tidn right. Tidn prapper. Why idn you at school? You mitchin' again?"

"I got ring worm."

"You always got something. Well, could be worse. Could be tape worm."

"Or lug worm," laughed her teenage daughter coming up behind me and pulling the balaclava down over my eyes. Her collie-cross planted a wet kiss on my bare knees.

The frozen rutted mud was iron-hard under the snow of Stuggy Lane. Sheep had gone ahead of me, leaving their polished droppings like figs spilt on a white tablecloth. A cock pheasant jumped out of the hedge and ran off and I chased him but he soon disappeared round the bend, his legs yellow blurs of panic. And the paleolithic boy that crouched in my twentieth-century body would have killed him and eaten him for all his gaudy plumage and love of life.

Many sheep sheltered beside the stacks on Broome Park. They regarded me from masks of resignation and shifted nervously where the snow was churned khaki by hooves and urine. Their faces were nice, like the faces of judges pleasantly stoned on port or those happy slightly loony Pre-Raphaelite angels. Tony called them Mazed Muttonheads and punched them between the eyes at the dipping. But if anyone was a mazed muttonhead it was Tony with his debts and his bad marriage and the misery he tried to hide beneath bluster and obscenity.

It would have been good to have had Aurora with me to share my thoughts and feelings. The sheep reminded me of her. There was no guile in their eyes. And moving along the high pastures I continued to dream of Aurora while her radiance rose from the valley like the breath of freshly minted snow. Her smile danced before me, little pieces of liquorice wedged in the gap between her front teeth, a phantom of delight, like a wraith of fragrance released from new-baked bread. Kneeling in the snow, I wrote "I LOVE AURORA" with my fingertip and got up sporting orange and blue cold-blossoms on my knees.

The sky was full of snow. I climbed the last fieldgate and plodded up the bracken-tufted steeps of Cider Mill Hill to the dead oak. From the hilltop I could look back over the sweep of meadows to the railway embankment and the sea into another approaching squall. Standing in the sky, amongst the rush of woodpigeons' wings was like being adrift in the cosmos. But the grandeur of the universe puzzled me. Perhaps growing up was also a growing towards an understanding of the beauty of creation. Beautiful animals and birds, beautiful world. In the valley the timeless Brueghel figures were gathered round a bonfire by the hedge they were laying. Pruning, cutting, laying back – the ancient job of doctoring the hedges continued as it had in my father's boyhood. The old song, different singers, sacks round their shoulders, balaclavas under slouch hats or berets, leather jerkins and gaitered legs. Yes, "Hunters in the Snow" like the men in the picture Miss Lee had pinned up in her classroom. Watching them encircling the flames I had my first intimations of immortality in a Wordsworthian sense. Truly something comes from beyond self to illumine our vision of the physical world and during childhood our spirits refuse to put up barriers. The universe glowing luminous at night bequeaths a kind of acquiescence and wisdom. And yet while I gazed down through my dreams the "Hunters" by their bonfire were probably cursing the weather or gossiping about a neighbour or talking football. But I was reading Hugh Lofting's Doctor Doolittle books and daubing everything I encountered with the most primitive idealism. I wanted a world of talking animals and human kindness and a countryside secure forever behind hedges. The buzzard falling down the sky carried all my passion and longing. I could hear the past speaking to me in the whisper of drifting snow and the sighing of the oak twigs. Then, when the valley glittered white, my boyhood rang with rapture too great for one small spirit to bear.

*   *   *

Another thaw brought drizzle to the south west but the temperature dropped quickly again and the rain froze as it settled. The beauty of Clennon, where the woods and hedges had become ice sculptures and the meadows' gemlike glitter hurt the eyes, did not endure for long. By the beginning of March the frozen slush in the streets and the greying snow on the hills had lost its appeal. Emaciated sheep, dead birds and the cold and darkness belonged to a dead season and like everyone else I found myself yearning now for spring. The ringworm had cleared up and I was back at Jubilee Street Primary where *educare* meant many things but not "to bring up". Eventually the heavy rains fell and the snow melted. Clennon flooded in places six feet deep and we paddled across it in soapboxes baulked with rope and putty. All about us the seabirds and wildfowl billowed like dark smoke.

10
Blackbirds and Butterflies

I thought spring had come but I was wrong. A sudden vicious north wind whitened Clennon and the primroses looked embarrassed in the hedge bottoms.

"It won't last long," Mam said. "When the snow melts all the fields will be green again."

"Like they were last year," said Dad, "and the year before and the year before and –"

"You ought to be in the circus, Perce," Mam snapped. "All you need is a clown's hat – you've got the nose."

"Starkey, Knight and Ford stuck that on my face, Gerry." Mam's name was Gertrude but he had softened it to something sweeter and more intimate.

"Why haven't I got any brothers and sisters, Dad?"

"You put us off, boy. You looked like a Jap drill sergeant. God, you were ugly!"

The colour had deepened in Mam's cheeks and I wondered why she looked so hurt. Dad put an arm round her shoulders and cleared his throat and made as if to speak but changed his mind. In the face of such sudden and unexpected tenderness I felt an intruder.

Rain fell through the blackbird's song. Then there was just the soft hiss of the sky descending and puddling in the lane.

Winter was hanging about on Cider Mill Hill, chilling the field corners and browning the primrose petals. And under the elms by Broome Linhay an old neglected cow was dying of a disease. Butch and I looked at each other and he sighed and pushed his hands into the slit pockets of his jerkin. The cow coughed and wobbled on her legs and I knew she was following us with her eyes as we walked away.

"Are you sure it's a sparrow hawk?" I said.

"Colin showed it me in the bird book," he replied. "Doodlebug had the poor sod in his mouth and the bird was peckin' his head."

"Is it badly hurt?"

"Nope – but it's wonky on its legs and needs grub."

"Small birds," I mused and Butch patted his catapult and nodded.

We made half a dozen clean kills beside the ricks at Broome Park. The sparrows seemed to be queueing up for the slaughter. Butch's grin pushed the freckles up round his ears. But drawing back the elastic and releasing it and seeing the little bodies somersaulting down the thatch had hollowed out my guts. They gathered in a chirping mass on the rick and we murdered them with ball-bearings.

It was all so obscenely simple until I botched the job and collected a live one. The cock sparrow lay in the palm of my hand fighting for breath. The small, dark head slowly wagged at me like it was stressing an awful amazement. Then blood beaded the tip of its beak and fell onto my flesh and the bird died. The nictating membrane sealed the brightness of eyes which a few moments before had held the day's wonder.

"Shitty sparrow-hawk," I quavered. And I left Butch with his pile of raptor's snacks and ran home growling up the self-disgust.

Yet Colin Yeo's hawk held me in thrall. It hopped around the chicken-wire mews, mad of eye and stiff of leg. Close up it had the manic, ruffled appearance of a cabinet minister. A couple of days after its tussle with Doodlebug it appeared to be fretting for the sky but applying the trade of smash-and-grab along the hedges did not go down too well at first. The sparrow hawk was getting more fresh meat than Dad and the roadside brambles held little attraction for the crafty tiercel. So we starved him for forty-eight hours and released him on the dump. This time he didn't palely loiter in the sedge.

"Yeo's peregrine ain't in his cage," O'Flaherty said.

"Sparrow-hawk," I said.

"Same bloody fing, ennit?" O'Flaherty hissed.

"Yes, Horseshit," I said. "They eat tom cats."

"Bloody 'ell! – wot sods!'

"We let the hawk go on Sunday, down Clennon. You want to buy my catapult?"

"How much?"

"Five bob."

"Leave off, Carter!"

"Half-a-crown?"

He nodded and took the catapult and said: "I'll owe it you."

*   *   *

"Good," Granny smiled. "I like sparrows, killing little things like they idn nice."

"Sparrows eat grain," Grandad sneered. "They're vermin, Em."

"They're little birds."

"For Christ's sake!"

He had the peculiar henhouse b.o. of a man who bathed once a month – under protest.

"Sparrows," he added, upper lip curling.

And I could see him potting Prussians and ducking whizz-bangs and quibbling his mandibles like the bloody old snowy owl. All that old time religion was phoney. It was stupid to expect him to be diminished even slightly by the death of a sparrow.

Beyond the steamy backroom window spring was not exactly burgeoning. A scattering of blackthorn blossom brightened the hedges, rooks were patching up their nests at Aish and green arrow-heads of celandine leaves had appeared in Clennon's marsh. The rest was messy – a boiled cabbage countryside recovering from a heavy cold.

"I love this poem, Brian," said Miss Lee. "What made you write it?"

(What makes you go to the lavatory or sneeze or sigh?)

> "A tall tree up there
> and one cloud on the hill,

and the horse munching grass
and the sun standing still."

"Pity we haven't a school magazine," Miss Lee smiled. "Do
your Mum and Dad know you write poetry?"

"Yes, miss."

"And Mr Greensleeves?"

I shrugged. Greensleeves worshipped the academic smart-
arses like David Kellerman who was Oxbridge potential and
could do algebra as easily as I could assemble doggerel.

"Does Mr Greensleeves like your poetry?"

"No, miss. Well, I haven't showed it him."

"Why ever not?"

But she knew why and changed the subject.

The headmaster had never heard of the Mabinogion but he
was keen on Greek mythology. Leaning forward he took his
weight on his fingertips, mantling our desk like a big bird of
prey. His smile lacked humour – the proverbial Cheshire cat
quizzing a mouse. We had been discussing the centaurs and
Butch had come close to nodding-off. Mr Greensleeves had
sensed his boredom and angled patiently for the opportunity of
introducing the bamboo.

"Tell me, Meredith," he whispered, swaying on his arms and
lidding his eyes. "Tell me the name of the mythical creature
that was half human, half animal."

Butch flashed me the quickest of panic-striken glances and I
masked the whisper behind the hand I had brought up to scratch
my nose.

"Please sir," Butch bellowed, " – Buffalo Bill."

"You and Carter can go to my study, Meredith," Mr Greensleeves smiled, and he cocked his head and looked at me sideways like a hooded crow.

I am certain he believed you could stimulate growth of moral
fibre by building team spirit in a rabble. Anyone with grit and a
stiff upper lip could blunder through life using Baden Powell's
compass whenever the fog came down. I was good at ball games
but Mam kept those pursuits in perspective. She slyly suggested
they were public school card tricks designed to bemuse the lower
class. Our muscle was required to keep the flag flying over the
colonies. But I'm glad we were persuaded to applaud virtue on
the football field and on the street corner. Miss Lee understood
because she thought with the heart and loved us. She knew how

to push kindness into me to get the rainbows of response. O'Flaherty never saw the dog star or the sun rise from the sea. His world was a nothingness of self lost in self, a universe of self. He was the Che Guevara of the backstreets minus a political philosophy or a single idea. It was he who stole Mrs Hannaford's bra off the clothes lines and stuffed it with straw and put it on Bickford's scarecrow. Watching him, eyes drowsy with laughter, time ruptured and lost even its glacial impetus. A year really was a very long time, a biblical exaggeration. Then, the coming of the swallows and cowslips yellowing the meadows by the dump and a cuckoo calling from the top of the Marist Convent beech.

I was ten on April 3rd and all the kids except O'Flaherty came to my party. Mam would not have the primary school Dillinger in our home. So while we were at the Picture House he raided Old Man Forsey's garden and stuck a huge plasticine willie on the tree'd gnome.

PC Tarr pretended it was a serious crime.

"I didn't do it," I said. "I was at the pictures with Colin Yeo, Butch Meredith and everyone else."

"You could have done it on the way home."

"Honest we didn. We went straight up the chip shop."

"You'd better speak to that cockney horror, O'Flaherty," Mam said. "He wasn't at the party."

"Was it him, Brian?" said PC Tarr.

"I dunno."

"OK," he smiled, fastening the top button of his tunic. "I'll have a word with Johnny O'Flaherty."

"Words," Mam snorted. "All that sod understands is a boot up the arse."

"Mr Forsey said the same about Brian," confessed PC Tarr.

"Let him bloody try," Mam bayed, but her glare sent me over the back gate as soon as she had gone to the front door with the policeman.

*   *   *

That spring Colin, Butch and I spent a couple of long weekends on the sea cliffs between Scabbacombe Head and Inner Froward Point. We humped the most bizarre camping equipment on our backs from the bus stop by the toll house along the lanes past Nethway and Kingston towards the English Channel.

The hedges were full of purple orchids, bluebells and the soft green leaves of bracken and hawthorn. Seen from the gateways luminous green fields and more hedges curved down into the valley. Larks trilled and insects droned and the swifts hunted high. Beyond the great bracken-decked headland the sea rushed to meet the horizon and we could smell it wafting across the scent of grass and the reek of sheep. The surface of the lane was braided with cattle dung.

"We're nearly there," Colin said. It was his place. His dad had brought him there fishing during the war and Colin could handle a rod and he knew about the bass. Already he was a good angler.

A mud track pushed between heavy green banks and led us around the barn into the sheep field that was pitted and scarred with rabbit burrows and runs.

"Bliddy rabbits," Colin grinned. "Thousands of the lil sods. Us'll have a few by morning."

We reached the stream against the gone-wild hedge of alders and oaks and put up the tent under a canopy of leaves. The tent was not quite as waterproof as an old flour bag but it was necessary and all the proper explorers had one.

Butch and I laid the fire and Colin attended to the billycan of baked beans and spam mess. Away from the fire the evening closed bright and cool, and the surf lifted and crashed on Scabbacombe sands. We sat close to the heat in our cotton shirts and shorts and bare feet.

"You kin set the snares while I fish," said Colin.

After a moment's awkward silence Butch said:

"There idn any snares. We must 've left them at the bus stop."

Colin looked at me, sensing betrayal.

"Sorry, Col," I mumbled.

"You lyin' twat," he sneered and I hit him so hard the blood gushed from his nose and he rolled onto his back sobbing and clutching his face.

"Look, Col," I said. "The rabbits aren't important. There's still the fish and the gulls' eggs. I couldn't help it about the snares. Bloody hell! – you could've done it."

We shook hands because the friendship was hot behind our eyes and we went down to the beach where Colin cast prawns for bass but did not catch a fish.

Come dawn the feeding coneys were a grey hood on the upper
slopes of the valley. Before breakfast we plunged in the surf and
ran shivering back to the fire. A pair of fulmars were inspecting
Scabbacombe Head and the constant jabber of kittiwakes lofted
from Down End Point. Butch and I crammed some old newspapers in our gas mask bags and set off to traverse the rocks
under the cliffs. Colin remained on the beach, pitting his skill
against the bass that came nosing through the surf.

Soon we were picking up gulls' eggs, leaving the nests of
three untouched and concentrating on the singles. There were
colonies of kittiwakes, razorbills and guillemots beneath the
cliff top spinney of scrub elm, alders and thorns. Above
the loomeries cormorants sat, wings outstretched to catch the
morning sun. We moved quietly below the rock walls in case the
auks panicked and knocked their eggs off the ledges. The shale
was wet and slippery with weed but almost every cleft and
hollow had its nest of plaited grass holding the beautifully
mottled herring gulls' eggs.

Down End Point rolled up to meet the farmland in a mass of
furze and bracken, and here the adders lay entwined, too sun-
drugged to move.

"Crikey," Butch said. "I don't like snakes and I don't like
heights. I wish I'd stayed home. There's a cowboy on at the
Palladium."

But the gulls' egg harvest kept him interested.

Among the boulder jumbles under the cliffs the pickings
were good and Butch seemed happier. I showed him the house
martin colony in the roof of the cave, and the precipice the fox
had zig-zagged up one unforgettable autumn day during the war.

"Why do we have to go so high?" Butch mewled, closing his
eyes and clinging to the cliff top barbed wire. I shook my head,
unable to comprehend his distress. The beauty of nature was my
narcotic and people who weren't hooked appeared odd.

When we had waded through the chin-deep gorse to the
fields and emerged hot and scratched Butch registered defeat.

"I'm going back to Col," he said, and I could see the morning
had passed him by so I went alone to the sward on the other side
of the deep inlet which was littered with rabbits' bones, the
skulls of sea birds and grubbed-out bluebell bulbs. All the badger
paths converged at the sett behind the withered elderberry tree
on the promontory. Generations of brocks had added their

bedding to the spoil heap and roamed through the night wind along the ancient trails, the same trails I was using to take me across the cliff tops. I could see the animals in my mind's eye, their fur blazing with little flames of moonlight, ambling up to the fields to pass among the sheep.

The sun seared my head and brought a glow to my limbs. A screaming cloud of gulls frothed up from the loomeries and mutes showered around me.

"Bloody old shite hawks," I grinned and lowered myself down the vertical rock to make hair-raising trips along the ledges a hundred feet above the sea. In the deep shadows I clenched my teeth and hummed "Rule Britannia" but the tension of dancing over crumbly rock that was smeared with bird droppings had my body quivering. Butch would have fainted at the sight of me clinging to the dark face surrounded by gulls and jackdaws.

Then the bag was three-quarters full and the eggs snug in their newspaper wrappings. I surfaced from the shadows into glorious sunlight and walked over the cushions of thrift and sea campion to Shipwreck Cove for a long soak in the waterfall. Eventually the cold forced me out of the lemonade fizz to dry-off on one of the slabs of shale where mallow and sea kale grew. Later I found a mallard's nest with thirteen eggs in the pebbles above the tideline but they were all close to hatching.

The great black-backed gulls barked and boomed and flapped away from the rock whose tenancy they had held ruthlessly since the last ice age. Their eggs were twice the size of herring gulls' eggs and Dad reckoned they had a different flavour, gamey and "moorish". The so-called fishy flavour was an old wives' tale, and the yolks creamed thick and orange when Mam beat them into omelettes and served them with plenty of pepper and brown bread.

I slid down the bluebell steeps on my behind and descended the narrow rock chimney to the clitter by jamming my elbows and knees against the sides. Now I was free to plunder Gull Rock and top up my bag with half a dozen new laid black-backs' eggs, swinging round overhangs and working my way up holds just large enough to accommodate fingertips and toes. The summit was a bit larger than our dining room table and I lay there for an hour or two and ate my snack and watched the birds flashing by like sword strokes. Solitude provoked an intense thirst for adventure.

"Why aren't you interested in tigers?" Miss Lee asked during Nature Study.

"Dunno, Miss. I suppose it's because you don't see tigers in Clennon Valley. I don't like palm trees and jungle stuff and foreign animals. And I don't like Tarzan's American accent. But I love badgers and foxes."

"Tell the class about a fox," she smiled. "Go on – give us a five-minute talk."

I tried to put the animal philosophy into words but it sounded daft and I didn't really want to share the more personal aspects with a bunch of grinning idiots. There in the classroom of small desks with its high ceiling and windows placed out of reach I spoke of my dream of the secret animal death on the hill top. And they laughed, everyone except Sonia Johnsie, Aurora and Miss Lee.

"Crow bones on Cider Mill Hill!" Clarke Herbert guffawed and I gobbed right in the centre of of his big red face.

"Miss," he roared. "M-i-i-isss."

The oyster of phlegm crept down his nose and was yo-yo'ing from the tip when Mr Greensleeves burst in like an American marine and took us single-handed. The caning was OK because Clarke shared it – for shouting.

*   *   *

The Merediths boiled Butch's gulls' eggs despite Mam's warning and Mrs Meredith took the top off her's to find an eye and a tiny beak amongst the mesh of cooked blood vessels.

"Dad hit me round the ear with his slipper," Butch morosely informed us.

"You got to crack the eggs to see if they'm set," said Colin. "They idn like chickens' eggs."

"Anyway. I bet the buggers are fishy," Butch said.

I stuck my thumbs under the straps of my backpack and kept quiet. Fine weather emptied the streets and Butch came to the sea cliffs because he could not stand his own company.

"We should've brought Aurora," Colin said and I quickened my pace to get ahead of them, wishing I was the old dancing fox. If you walked fast enough you could slip into the mirage and let it whisk you back to Avalon.

"Aurora."

I was lying among the bluebells on the sloping side of Scabbacombe Head. Directly below me a kestrel hunted the fringe of the cliff. The flicker of pointed wings and the turn of the fierce little mouse-hawk's head decided the fate of cockroach and vole. Aurora's ghost sailed away out to sea and vanished.

Far above the four hundred feet shoulder of Scabbacombe a pair of buzzards circled and even higher a few white smudges of cirrus were printed on the blue. The day was very warm and the afternoon calm twinkled on the sea. Bumble bees floated by and "kee-kee" cried the kestrel as he lifted over the spinney displaying plumage the colour of September stubble, October bracken and November's plough. Guillemots and razorbills whirred low over the water and the black-backs dredged up their booming cries. My sunburnt face took kindly to the sea breeze that was rising to lick across the bracken fronds. The wavelets breathed on the rocks below. Then something dark eclipsed the sun, briefly, like a drift of smoke. A host of peacock butterflies fluttered in from the Channel they had crossed and settled exhausted upon the bluebells, the brambles and my face. It was a Mabinogion miracle for I did not know the butterflies were migrants. I thought I was a chosen one and the creatures were telling me that my love of nature would not go unrewarded. Butterflies rose wherever I put my feet and they swirled and scattered about me on the wind as I climbed to meet the larksong. . . .

The sea of evening glittered and swung and shimmied and lurched. Its surface was barred with cobalt blue, dark green and mother-of-pearl like the side of a fabulous mackerel. And floating over the dazzling waves came the gulls, their pinions like spread fingers of quicksilver. Big flocks straggled down the shadowy headland and the last slanting rays of the sun caught the fields above our camp. The scent of crushed bluebells and bracken went with me into the valley.

"I caught some fish," Colin said and he held up a pollock. The firelight twinkled on golden scales.

"Pollock and bass," Colin continued joyfully.

The sky darkened and the flames grew brighter. Butch stared at the fire and sniffed and drew his sleeve across his nose. Throughout the night he shivered under his thin blanket, body clenched in a tight comma of misery. Against the noises of the wild – the sigh of surf and the murmur of gulls – the frenzied castanetting of his teeth helped Colin and I feel very smug inside our eiderdowns.

11

Dartmoor

The tree behind the allotment hedge was the shrike's larder. Crawling through the tangle of saplings and briars I saw the mouse impaled on the blackthorn and heard the butcher bird alarming from the nearby thicket. Spring was not all dawn choruses and nature in a perpetual state of erection but what I discovered outside Paignton pushed me into excitement that was bad for my nerves. I lay awake at night afraid to close my eyes and admit the nightmares; and soon the lack of sleep produced the familiar hallucinations.

"It's far from normal," Mrs Penk said with some justification. Then, seeing the anger blaze white in Mam's face she added hastily: "Poor little mite! Hitler's got a lot to answer for."

"The boy needs bags of fresh air and rest," said Dr Thorpe for the thousandth time. "A few days away from home would help."

Just as the Swiss mountains could magic away tuberculosis Dartmoor's windy acres were said to hold palliatives for "nerves". And one Wednesday Mam and I took the Western National bus to Buckfastleigh where yet another of Dad's vast tribe of distant relatives collected us in a dusty Ford Prefect.

We were driven along the narrow, high-hedged road to Holne and up through the gate onto the open moor. Mam and

"Auntie" Eve gossiped and laughed while the countryside grew very thrilling and the hedges became banks of thorn and on every side great sweeps of grass and heather rolled unrestricted to the sky. Lower Tor Farm nestled in a coombe at the end of a lane that gave up when it reached the out-buildings and the pond. The sun was conjuring wild flowers from the hedge below the vegetable garden. I could smell the sunlight on the cuckoo pints, primroses, cow parsley, nettles and grasses. Finches bent the creamy corymbs of the elderflowers and a robin sang among the garlic mustard, loudly for such a small bird. But above the farmstead the moors quivered and beckoned under larksong and the three days I spent with my kin blurred and vanished in a flash so eager was I to harvest every experience. Cousin Walter Chubb had his own pony and let me ride it bareback. The first trick I attempted was a jump of Grand National proportions. For a while the Chubbs feared my crumpled silence on the grass the other side of the hedge meant another funeral. They had witnessed the separation of boy from mount, had gawped at my parabola over the thorns and had run from the house expecting to find a corpse. The bruised shoulder and hip, and the chipped front tooth did not curb my recklessness but after galloping Girlie the pony into a bog and seeing her rescued with ropes and tractor I was forbidden to ride unaccompanied.

My behaviour impressed Walter who was a burly thirteen-year-old, fascinated by willies – horses', bulls', dogs', mine but most of all his own which he was forever fondling. Many a time I caught him in the cowshed or hayloft making love to his fist and wearing the blissful, mindless expression of Stan Laurel.

When he could be coaxed away from his enervating hobby he borrowed his dad's hack and took me to wild places like Huntington Warren, the Swincombe Valley and Fox Tor Mires. I fell hopelessly in love with Dartmoor and its quiet grandeur visited me in the classroom and in the back streets. The short stay at Lower Tor Farm lit a passion I shall carry to the grave.

*   *   *

"You're always 'ome ill," O'Flaherty complained, prising open my fist to "borrow" some sweet coupons.

" 'Ere," he added in the low, deadly voice that spelt trouble. "Wot you gonna do wiv them tadpoles, Merediff?"

Butch shrugged. It was his way of saying: What the hell do

you do with tadpoles? You plop them in the jar and they swim round and slowly turn into frogs. The question was stupid.

"Hold 'em up. Let's have a better look."

O'Flaherty took a dozen steps backwards and drew the catapult from his hip pocket. Butch's face was the colour of the whitewashed wall. Slowly he hoisted the jam jar up on the string and held it away from him. O'Flaherty smiled, loaded the ball-bearing and drew the sling back to the lobe of his left ear.

"Please Horseshit," Butch whispered.

"Keep still," said O'Flaherty. "I don't want to hit you by mistake."

He held his breath, fired and the jar exploded and Butch groaned.

"Spot on!" O'Flaherty cried. "Bloody bulls eye."

Then he was leaving the ground on the toe of Dad's boot and dashing up the alley clutching his behind and howling obscenities.

"Get a cup of water, Bri," Dad said, and we retrieved all Butch's tadpoles except a couple O'Flaherty had crushed as he ran.

"That young spiv will end up on a rope," Dad went on. "Keep away from him – both of you. He's not sixteen ounces."

The potato whizzed past my ear and exploded on the side of Dad's head. He staggered, blinked and looked over his shoulder in amazement. O'Flaherty had done a complete circuit of the terrace and was standing at the bottom of the steps, two fingers of scorn held aloft.

"I'll kill the sod," Dad grated and he set off on what proved to be an epic chase.

We followed at a respectable distance, afraid Horseshit might mistake us for Dad's allies. The cockney's scrawny legs carried him quickly over the first hundred yards but Dad had the air of an experienced hound, confident of his stamina and ability to nail the quarry. By the time they had passed St Andrew's Church en route to the harbour the gap between them was thirty yards and Horseshit was tiring.

"I'm going to tan your arse till it's like a bit of liver, O'Flaherty," Dad panted.

"Bollocks," Horseshit gasped and we had to admire his pluck.

At the Hydro Hotel Dad was a mere ten lengths adrift and

closing fast. We straggled along behind, giggling and belching and loving O'Flaherty's humiliation.

The cockney psycho drew from some hidden fund of energy and sprinted across the green. Dad's head rolled as he too accelerated. The genteel tourists sitting on the sea wall turned to watch the closing stages of the race.

"I hope your Dad murders him," Butch snarled. "I hate O'Flaherty. I hate him."

It was high tide and the slipway and steps at the end of the prom were awash. Into the sea splashed the resourceful O'Flaherty and out he waded until the water lapped his chin. Dad hesitated, looked at the rise and fall of the swell and decided he was too old for such capers.

"You'd better run every time you see me, boy," he roared, shaking his fist at Horseshit who had never ventured out so deep before.

"You've won the battle but I'll win the war."

"Piss off," O'Flaherty said.

But Dad hung around for a quarter of an hour to make sure the monster was chilled to the bone.

"Let me know if he tries anything," Dad said on the way home. Butch glanced at me and I winked and tried to con myself that Dad's protection wasn't similar to Mickey Mouse offering to prevent Al Capone from attacking Pluto and Donald Duck.

"Maybe Johnny Pym will help," Butch said, swinging up into the branches of the chestnut tree.

Johnny was fourteen and treated O'Flaherty with the contempt of a veteran hardcase.

"Remember what he did to Horseshit up the playing field?"

"But why should he help us?"

"I'll get Brenda to speak to him."

"What if I have a go at Horseshit," I said.

"He'd bloody mangle you," Butch sneered.

"I'd just like a chance to hurt him a bit."

"You're dotty, Bri. Horseshit's got a lot of thatch loose. You can hit him with a brick and he grins and kicks you in the balls."

"I don't want to fight him," I admitted. "Only it idn right to keep on letting him get away with it."

We sat in the top of the tree and the spring evening faded golden and soft green as if we were in a bathysphere three fathoms down in the Caribbean. O'Flaherty hurried furtively up the lane muttering under his breath and casting about like a ferret.

"D'you really think Brenda would speak to Johnny?" I whispered.

Butch nodded and peered through the leaves to make sure O'Flaherty wasn't lurking in ambush.

"Why didn't he stay in London?" Butch sighed when the coast was clear.

"What! – in the Blitz!" I said. "He would've been killed."

"I know," Butch said wistfully.

On Friday evening I hired Colin Yeo's bike for half-a-crown promising to return it Saturday night. The machine was a small black wreck with a wobbly back tyre and a front light. But there was no bell and no three speed and no mud guards and no brakes.

"Mind you don't go too far," Mam said.

We were sitting on the garden bench catching the last of the sun and listening to the chickens and pigeons. The chimney sweep had called and there was still a faint whiff of soot in the back room. Doodlebug minced over the shed roof and approached Nibs amorously only to receive a set of claws in the nose for his trouble. Mam and I laughed.

"Can I have a bike, Mam?"

"If you pass your Eleven Plus."

"*When* he passes his Eleven Plus," Dad said from the lavatory.

"Don't forget to pull the chain, Perce," said Mam.

"Get rid of those crocodiles' eggs," I giggled.

"You'll pass your Eleven Plus for Mam, won't you Bri?"

"Why's it so important?" I said.

"Are you mad!" she cried. "Why is it important! Christ, boy! Do you want to go to Tweenaway like the rest of the bloody blockheads?"

"Tweenaway's OK," I said. "Butch wants to go there. Johnny Meredith says it's great."

"Speak to him, Perce."

Dad pulled the chain and emerged from the green door.

"You keep reading and writing and doing your sums," he said. "And you'll go to Torquay Grammar."

"Miss Lee had promised to give him some school work when he's home," Mam said. "She thinks he's definitely Grammar material. He's got my brains."

"I wondered where they'd gone," Dad laughed.

Our house was happy and noisy and there was blood in the stones. Pain, misery and some poverty entered our home but didn't linger. I suppose we had so little to lose we could face up to anything Fate threw at us.

Leaving my bed at dawn I felt the loneliness in the deserted streets and nearly changed my mind. But presently I was free-wheeling down the straight hill to Longcombe Cross and the freshness of the new day stroked my skin and stirred all the radiant shades of green around me.

"I love you. I love you. I bliddy love you" – fox, rabbit, bird, stream, hedge, field, sky; the bits and pieces of God's physical being.

I pedalled through Totnes and Dartington to Buckfastleigh. The sun shone upon my back and my shadow danced before me into the lateral shadows of the trees all the way to Holne. Coming over I'd met the lark-song and the solitude and saw the pregnant pony mares and heard the cat-calls of the buzzards and the softer fluting of curlew. The road went up and down through dewy grass, heather and bracken. Looking eastwards I saw distant Hay Tor and the blue shadow of the Newbridge Valley. At Hexworthy smoke uncoiled from a chimney and blackfaced sheep congregated on the sward beside the gate that opened onto the Swincombe Valley. Cousin Walter had brought me here twice but he had not seen the merlin and even after I had pointed it out he had showed no interest.

"Bird," he scoffed. "So what? The moors are full of birds but they don't do you no good. They peck out the lambs' eyes."

I felt older than Walter despite the chronological gap. His eyes and ears and nose were pieces of redundant machinery.

"Give me a poetic comparison," said Mr Greensleeves. "Compare something with something to emphasize the difference. For instance: 'as different as chalk from cheese'."

"As different as snow from fire, sir," I said eagerly.

"Where did you get that from, Carter?"

"I made it up, Sir. I got it out of my head."

"Yes, but which book put it there?"

"I made it up. The girls were as different as nettle from primrose."

"You made it up," smiled Mr Greensleeves. "Well go to my study and think about it, Carter."

"Think about what, Sir?"

"The book, Carter – the book."

Dartmoor pulsed and rippled in the heat. I left my bike against the drystone wall and walked through the succulent bracken fronds. Grass, whortleberry bushes and heath spread and vanished into haze. And cutting noisily through the hot, itchy days was the River Swincombe, a torrent of bronze water not much wider than a railway track.

I kicked off my daps and waded into a pool until the water washed around my knees. The merlin tiercel flew upstream and grabbed the rock pipit in flight without too much fuss. Perhaps it hadn't seen me but more likely it did not care what I was or it assumed I was as wingless and harmless as a tree rooted in the dead world.

Where two streams met on the margins of Fox Tor Mires a heron was patiently scanning the mud. The sight of me was enough to send it up and away leaving a "craarnk" of protest on the air. This was merlin country and tramping over it with Walter I had found the granite stump used by the birds as a plucking post. The little falcons were busy robbing the sky of larks and pipits. Why was Arthur's wizard friend called Merlin? "Merddin," Mam corrected me. "The double d is pronounced like the 'th' in 'thee'." But I saw a sharp-faced, beady-eyed, old celt reading the landscape and the weather and people's hearts. Merlin – such a lovely name. To own an egg of the noble little raptor would be very satisfactory. And I would possess a talisman.

Among the red leaves of cotton grass I came upon the decapitated body of a lark and there were many feathers around the plucking post. The nest had to be close at hand. I knew it before the landscape presented the evidence. From the slope near Childe's Tomb it was possible to lie unobserved and look down on the mires. Midges danced round my head and lapwings called from the marshes of Peat Cot. Twice the merlin tiercel came to the plucking post to dress the carcasses of small birds and each occasion was followed by a visit to the nearby reeds. I marked the spot and never took my eyes off it as I ventured into the bog. The tiercel said "kik-kik" and was gone but the falcon remained anchored to the ground by strong instincts until I was nearly upon her, then she leapt up and fled.

I knelt and parted the grass to uncover the scrape under

a dome of stems. There were five eggs – reddish brown and blotched and speckled with a darker brown. I took one and pierced it and sucked out the meat. My throat was dry and my hand shook as I tucked the egg into the tobacco tin. Then I moved off, quickly, in case the birds became frightened and abandoned the site. Raking the grass seeds off my legs I headed down the Swincombe and cycled to Combestone Tor to eat my sandwiches. Shining through everything I did was the joy of possessing the merlin's egg. I would take it from the cotton wool and hold it and lick it to digest the hawk magic. No other boy in Paignton or Torquay or Brixham could boast such treasure.

I cycled home under the rich blaze of evening. Soon Hexworthy and Ventor Reservoir were behind me and I rattled down to Holne. The white of wild parsley and stitchworth lay among blue drifts of germander speedwell in the hedges. A cuckoo called repeatedly from the copse by the village and beyond, South Devon was a chorus of retiring birds. It was like sailing into Elgar's music and I wished it could have gone on forever. I pushed the bike up the steepest hills and rolled down to secret coombes which were lit by hawthorn blossom. Towards Totnes evening hazed into dusk and from the top of Bridgetown Hill I looked back to the high reef of moorland. The same pale western sky and the one bright star I could see above the tors were mirrored in the merlin's eyes.

12
Glazed Horizons

That summer Aurora terminated our love affair and transferred her favours to Paul Quantick – a heavily freckled Lothario destined for a career in the Co-op grocery section. She might have continued as my squaw until the end of term if I hadn't released the loudest fart ever heard in the Regent Cinema and been frog-marched out by a couple of pugnacious usherettes. It was during a romantic love scene and the stalls erupted.

"I heard about it," Dad said. The steam from the boiled potatoes only partially hid his grin.

"And you think it's funny," Mam snapped. "Something to boast about over the pub. You want him to get on but you won't stop him behaving like a gutter-snipe."

"Toffs fart," said Dad.

"Not while Walter Pidgeon is kissing Greer Garson."

"What was the film?"

"Blossoms in the Dust."

"Should have been *Gone with the Wind*," he said.

"Don't you care how he grows up, Perce?"

"Yes, but there's a hell of a lot of important things wrong with the world and he doesn't have to accept all the bullshit and snobbery. The zombies are in control producing more bloody zombies."

"Purping in the cinema isn't exactly a world-shattering event," Mam said, close to laughter.

Beneath the clown's mask Dad was the frustrated scholar, far removed from the ordinary terrace denizen. He was a fallen angel denied by a lack of higher education a place next to Socrates, Milton, Wilkie Collins, Thomas Hardy and William Frith (his favourite artist) at God's feet. The system had ripped off his wings before he had spread them and left him to contemplate what might have been among the allotments and backyards. He fancied a life-style incorporating oak panelled study, library and spacious gardens and wine cellar.

Over the years he had assembled a collection of nearly six hundred books on a hit or miss basis. *The Canterbury Tales* stood between a tattered copy of *Men Only* and *Rose Gardening for Gentlefolk*. Maybe he did have a mind like a rag-and-bone merchant's yard but he could recognize mediocrity and never pretended the working class was an army of saints, martyrs and heroes. His wit was constantly employed chopping arrogant brickies, labourers and plasterers down to size as well as castrating wealthy drones.

Above all Dad lamented a lack of financial independence. At heart he was an exiled Squire Allworthy pining for Fielding's long-gone country where scholarship went hand in hand with pox and the reek of pig dung.

*   *   *

Mr Greensleeves separated Butch and me and sat me next to the genius David Kellerman who read Einstein's *Relativity* for fun. He was a solemn, middle-aged kid, humourless, priggish, incapable of mischief. He was one of those hateful prodigies destined for the Civil Service or a Cambridge fellowship and he would become president of Mensa and do the *Times* crossword in ten minutes. But he could not write a poem or draw a dandelion or kick a football or tell the difference between a rook and a crow. He would frown at me, trying to puzzle me out and I would put live grass-snakes in his desk and nettles in his daps. Then he would betray me to the headmaster and return to his equations.

The Kellermans were close friends and neighbours of the Forseys. They were well-off socialist grocers and subscribed fervently to state education but showed an unwillingness to meet the plebs on equal terms except at their place of business. Mr Kellerman tried to persuade Dad to make a new gate for his large property but wanted it done on the cheap and was told where to stick his money. Thus Dad's army of enemies grew, for integrity is always feared in others if absent in self.

Mrs Forsey hated Dad partly because he was a coarse "have-not" but mostly because he wasn't servile. She also disliked Christ's background and union connections. The biblical Jesus whiffed of council houses and down-and-outs and wasn't a bit like the C of E Messiah. Her condescension and Mr Kellerman's aloofness rankled Dad but he maintained an impudent stance. Every so often the Kellermans and the Forseys saw him staggering home from the pub blowing raspberries at the moon and their God. Of course they pretended to be scandalized. Where the lights are brightest a pack of poodles may mock an old wolf.

*   *   *

Green things were rising from the heat. Swifts screamed on the wing, sunlight sprang across the grass and the moors sprawled anaesthetized under a very blue sky. Gradually, tramping out alone from Lower Tor Farm, I began to think Devon was the front garden of Avalon. Paradise could be experienced in breathing and running, in belonging to the elements. It was around me and there under a whispering green ceiling of bracken. Glazed horizons called to me and roused a yearning which would remain unsatisfied. A buzzard hacking the air with its wings escaped from the shimmering wet-look of heat enfolding the tor. The sharp cry gutted the day and the iron of sound honed into a scream prickled my skin. Curlew and plover lifted like hair on the hill's nape and the buzzard killed a young rabbit and wrote the ancestral blood-script on bare granite. The mad-eyed, massive, sun-dripping hawks were waiting for me behind sleep that night. . . .

Another day opened with mist clinging to the whortleberry bushes and furze as I padded up the sheep path to see the sunrise from Hay Tor. Below me thousands of acres of South Devon were veiled in unearthly light, like the glow of a corpse. A curlew called its sweet double note that subsided into bubbling song. Then the sun came red out of the sea and I was the sun-child sailing over the coombes and tors to meet Arthur and Merlin.

"If I wanted to write poetry," Kellerman said, casting a

jealous eye across my work, "I would. It's not clever or difficult."

"How would you like a kick in the balls, big head?" I said.

Confronted by such tremendous logic he buried his head
between the covers of *The Origin of Species* or whatever he was
reading.

> "Gold is the morning sun
> and gold is the buzzard's eye.
> Like a dark cross he hangs
> in the Eastern sky.
> And the spirit part of me
> will join him when I die."

"I saw the old hawk, Miss – last Sunday up Hay Tor."

"Are you going to finish it?"

"It is finished, Miss."

"Yes," she said quietly, reading it again. "Of course it is.
May I keep it, Brian?"

"Yes – it's for you anyway, Miss."

"Poems!" O'Flaherty snorted when Butch told him. We were
peering over the harbour rails down into the keep-pot. A tangled
mass of crabs shifted, waved their pincers and lived-out the final
hours of their lives before the cauldrons of boiling water des-
patched them to salads, paste jars or pâté tins.

"Carter the farter writes ditties."

The sneer twisted his face and made him look like Dracula's
nephew.

> " 'When the wind wouldn't blow
> and the ship wouldn't go
> – Carter the farter would start 'er.'

'– that's real po'try."

He smiled and ground the butt end of his cigarette into the
hand Butch had clamped to the rail. Butch's scream sent the
gulls scattering high and noisy.

"You mad bugger, O'Flaherty," I cried and caught him
smack in the face with a terrific right hook. Like something from
a Disney cartoon his eye swelled and closed instantly.

"Mad bugger," I grunted again and planted two swift jabs on
target.

"I'm goin' to massacre you, Farter."

But the kick was telegraphed and I flailed his head with more swinging blows and the primary school psycho staggered.

"Hit the shit out of him, Bri," Butch growled, scenting blood. And I moved in close to taste the sheer physical pleasure of knuckles pulping flesh and bone. Then something small but harder and heavier than a brick stopped me dead. The blood squirted from my nose all over O'Flaherty's shirt. He had hit me with a perfectly timed straight right and I could feel the aggression draining into my legs and jellying my knees.

Before the adrenalin burnt out I managed another swipe and Horseshit had a big ear to match his big eye. He also had a very big crow to pluck. Stuttering from the centre of a sulphurous rage he sprang and split his upper lip on my elbow.

"Christ," roared the berserk and the next moment I was the plaything of a frenzied wolverine. During the thirty seconds of my destruction I recall bits of my hair being yanked out and my head in O'Flaherty's grip beating a dull tattoo on the flagstones.

"For God's sake, Horseshit," I sobbed, and miraculously he released me but remained kneeling on my chest and whispered:

"You're a proper fart, Farter. What are you?"

"Piss off, O'Flaherty."

He lowered his face until it was a couple of inches from my own, squeezing the breath out of me with his knees. I opened my mouth and before I could close it O'Flaherty half-filled it with gob.

"Now get up, Fart," he smiled and I did, to retch and cough and glare at him.

"You bloody clown," he said, planting both fists deep in his pockets. But behind the facade of toughness I noted for the first time a definite absence of bounce.

We bathed in a tiny rock-strewn inlet called Fairy Cove just beyond the outer wall of the harbour. The overhanging sandstone was perforated with the holes of nesting sand martins and a score of little fork-tailed, brown and white birds danced against the cliff. Milky blue wavelets flopped onto the pebbles, wheezed up the beach and retired softly.

"Wotchergottinyerbag?" O'Flaherty asked Butch.

"Some salad rolls and a hard-boiled egg."

"I like eggs."

"You can have mine, Horseshit," Butch said hastily.

O'Flaherty sat there on the shingle, cupping the egg in his hands and gazing over the advancing tide.

"Why do the sea come in and go out?" he murmured.

"The moon pulls at it," I said.

"The moon ain't out."

"It's gravity and stuff," I said, wondering if his wounds were smarting as much as mine.

"The world doesn't make sense," he said. "Bloody planes flying around. Bloody sea."

On the way home we wore our towels like cloaks and pretended we were mates of Hereward the Wake. Probably for some reason buried in our prehistoric ancestry we were addicted to throwing things and it came as no surprise when O'Flaherty chucked the hard-boiled egg at the beach inspector who was cycling slowly by whistling "Annie Laurie". The egg made a funny noise on impact – a sort of explosive "squelk!" The beach inspector's feet slipped off the pedals and his puddings slammed down on the crossbar. For a long moment he remained transfixed, legs bowed and quivering and the knuckles of the fists clenched to the handlebar gleaming white. Then the bike fell to the ground and the poor little man executed a tap dance of agony, clutching his ruined matrimonial tackle and making strange mewing noises.

"Tell you what, Horseshit," I gasped, "I'm not a fart."

He sucked the mucus which seemed permanently lodged at the back of his nose down onto his tongue and spat hard against the lamp-post.

"Ain't you?" he grinned.

A group of old age pensioners gathered round the dancing beach inspector and we slouched away before they could put two and two together.

Summer was the fading of elder flower and the haymaking, the tedding and the stacking. Butch, Colin and I picked peas and lifted potatoes and singled turnips. In the midge-clouded heat we chopped away with our hoes, slack of mind and happy to plod through the summer like shire horses. But Dartmoor was my spiritual retreat and up there company was a burden.

*   *   *

The barn owls were two white blurs, a silent movie flicker – white, black, sepia, slowed down to create an image of beautiful violence. The evening of gentle sounds and colours smouldered away to mist.

Cousin Walter and his dad got out of the car and frowned at me.

"Where have you been?"

"Walking."

"I told 'ee Bri wadn lost, father," said Walter and his hand snaked into his trousers to begin another game of pocket billiards.

"But us wadn to know," said Uncle George.

"I saw the owls," I said. "We've got owls in Clennon Valley."

"Bliddy owulls," Walter laughed.

They were not really worried about my wanderlust. Uncle George said I got under his feet at the farm and he liked me best after dinner when I was drowsy and ready for bed.

One Sunday the Chubbs dropped Walter and me off at Emsworthy gate and we hiked down Houndtor Valley and the Becka Brook to the Leighon Ponds. I took a header into the water below the dam but my cousin was a non-swimmer and sat sulking in the noonday heat which was savage enough to discourage pocket billiards.

"Otters live here," he said. "The hunt killed one last week."

The information was calculated to hurt me.

"Why?" I said.

"Otter hounds kill bloody otters," he said, nettled.

"Like sausage dogs kill sausages," I smiled.

Flies swooped to greedy on my lips and nose. Walter flashed me a dirty look and dipped his handkerchief in the pond and applied it to his swollen, red, gnat-chewed face. But at the circle of stones he shook off his bad mood and spoke passionately about motorbikes. Up there on the high, round hill the breeze was cool and we sat hunched against the granite megaliths.

"When I leave school, I'm going to live here," I said.

"How bloody boring," said Walter. "Tis just a lot of old rocks and heather. You'm mazed, boy – mazed."

Towards the end of summer I saw the gleam of Sirius in the upper pond. Green dog star, dark-leaved woods, dew-spangled moors; and parting the black waters silently an otter swam with moonlight flashing silver on its head. It was a brief glimpse but enough. The ponds became a shrine at the gates of the holy place, and I would return to them year after year while the rest of the childhood countryside was gobbled up by houses, roads, car parks and caravan sites.

13
It's only a Badger

I loved my cat but when she came in head held high and proud and a dead robin in her jaws, I could have pulled out her fangs. It was sentimental and irrational and Dad kept me on the hook of his scorn for ages.

"Hawks and foxes can butcher birds by the ton," he concluded, "but poor old Nibs only has to go wild once in a blue moon and you're ready to put her down."

"She's overfed as it is," Mam said. "She don't need robins. Her belly's full of pout whiting."

"It's her instincts," Dad said. "If she was a tom we could have them cut off."

Nibs yawned, opening wide her little bucket mouth and holding the yawn and looking stupid in a drugged way. The dead robin lay wet and ruffled at her feet. She pawed it playfully and cocked her head until Dad scooped up the bird and took it outside. I sat staring blindly down at my plate and the first rains of autumn crept grey off the sea to drench the dusk.

1947 was the annus mirabilis. We had gas put in the three downstairs rooms that summer but the bedrooms were still candlelit. I would creep down through the darkness, the candle flickering and the shadows dilating, to use the lavatory while the night pressed around me blacker than a gestapo gaol. There

were great corners of nothingness for the imagination to fill
with ghosts and nameless horrors, but generally the night was
my friend and I liked to believe I was a soft-treading animal.

Small things are permanently stitched into my recollection
of those times: steam engulfing me on the wooden railway
bridge in the centre of town; cramming three farthings worth
of warm bread into my mouth, chunk by chunk at Saturday
morning cinema; Butch and I driving cattle in a jostling mass
along Dartmouth Road and causing traffic chaos; climbing Big
Tree and clinging to the top branch of the giant conifer one
hundred and fifty feet above the goods yard.

Jubilee Primary went into mourning on the death of little
Alison Williams who succumbed to peritonitis. Her brother
Roger stood in assembly keening like a gate swinging on rusty
hinges, and Miss Lee took him to the staff room for cake and
comfort. Paignton was a small community and Alison's death
sent ripples of bereavement out into the suburbs. But I knew she
had become part of the seasons and all that frail beauty lying in
the soil would soon be resurrected in bud and blossom and green
grass blade.

The big migrations of people from the North and Midlands to
our seaside town were still a trickle and I found the Devon
accent dominant everywhere – except during the summer.
Visitors continued to pour in on the Holiday Specials and in July
and August the beaches were packed. The ugly ironwork of
invasion defences had vanished from the sands but the war was
still more than a memory. It had been part of our lives for so long
– like a disease or a crippling injury. Now and then something
would surface from the subconscious to cloud a sunny morning.
The drone of a plane or the siren sounding for the fire engine
could conjure up the insecurity of the dark years and flood the
stomach swiftly into nausea. Then Dad told me we had lost
India and the Empire was finished but it meant very little to me.
England, which was Devon, was green and pleasant like the
country in the song. Hints of what life was like in the coalfields,
the industrial North and the slums of the big cities came from
Pathe News and Mam's eruptions of class resentment. But they
had no substance and were as remote as the fairy tales of the
Mabinogion. The media presented all strikers as villains and we
in the South West heard of the huge wage packets a miner or a
docker could earn and wondered why they wanted more. We

had been indoctrinated to accept our lot – the tin bath, the outside lav, the cramped back-to-back houses and every other social deprivation. It was the working class destiny, the losing number of a divine raffle. Higher education, given free and grudgingly, liberated us from "the rich man in his castle, the poor man at his gate" syndrome, and the day of the mindless "toff" who couldn't lace his own shoes or boil a kettle was over.

*   *   *

Ernie guided the plough team up and down the hillside. Edward and Solomon were sheathed in sunshine and lather and Ernie spoke to them gently under his cloud of gulls. I could not watch the heavy horses without the water coming to my eyes. Their comradeship, serenity and obedience were deeply appreciated by true horsemen like Ernie who had come out of the North East, ignorant of farming but possessing a blazing love of the animals. Observing them after their day's work was over, noting how they relished the field under their hooves and how they breasted the waves of scent thrown up by autumn, I knew they enjoyed the open air as I did. But the golden era of the shire was at an end. All over Britain the workhorse was betrayed and led to his death to finish up as glue and petfood. The tractors came rolling noisily from the stables, driving the ghosts of the shires before them to swell an enduring lament for the past. But Solomon, Bathsheba and Edward survived because although I did not know it Cider Mill Farm was doomed and was living out its last years. During the next decade the caravans would arrive and the barns, outbuildings and farmhouse would vanish – part of a greater betrayal.

So one old tractor and three horses were deemed enough to carry the old ways through the twilight years, and my shires escaped the poleaxe which brought tens of thousands of their kindred crashing lifeless to the cobbles of nackers' yards from Cornwall to Cumberland. "Pounds, Shillings and Pence" was the ultimate law governing human behaviour. It was bloodier and more merciless than anything the jungle could offer, and the shires who came full of trust to meet death as redundant machines knew nothing of the betrayal. With the letting of their blood we distanced ourselves even further from the pure animal men who slept in the grass like horses and spoke the language of wild beasts.

The blackberries were at an end. They sprang from the hedges like burst blood vessels on stalks and many were covered in cobwebby grey mould. I ate the crisp red ones and avoided the bright songbirds' eyes of fulsome berries whose flavour was strange as if poisoned by flies. And the rain fell in a continuous depressing downpour.

The bullen trees were stripped of their little yellow leaves by the equinoctial gales and became cages for small birds. If I didn't actually pray to a tree I stood before many a perfect ash while the music rang in me. Trees were everywhere then and we were seduced by nature and things outside the world – the moon, the sun and the stars.

"Who's this?" Miss Lee said, pointing at the boy in my picture.

"Me, Miss."

"And you're speaking to the moon and stars?"

"No, Miss. The horse is speaking to the sky and I'm trying to understand what he's saying."

She pinned it to the wooden partition that separated our class from Miss Gilcrest's class. We sat around taking off our gym shoes after a long session of folk dancing. Miss Lee had entered a group in the local dance festival for the coming spring and we practised three times a week, spinning and whooping, boys and girls, hands linked, forming circles. It was the school year of my Eleven Plus and Mr Greensleeves, anxious for a crop of prestigious Grammar school passes, had relented a little. And O'Flaherty's reign of terror if not at an end did not sully my life as it had done. He was wary of me now after his pyrrhic victory, although I did not push my luck. But beyond the playground, the back alleys and the neat suburban gardens the Middle Ages persisted.

At the back of the neglected orchard was a red earth bank topped with trees and shrubs and masked by brambles. Badgers had occupied a sett here since Dad was a boy, and I had seen the current tenants nosing out of summer dusks to sniff the air and grub for roots and beetles.

"There's a badger dig tomorrow," Enid Brinham said, folding her arms on the gate.

I pushed handfuls of grass into Solomon's face and tried to shut out her words.

"Badger digging isn't sport, Enid," said Ernie. "It's murder.

What do they get out of it anyway?"

"I dunno," Enid shrugged. "Farmer wants it. He idn fond of they old badgers."

Ernie clicked his tongue and snapped the reins, urging the team forward to cut a new furrow. The black-headed gulls screamed derisively at me.

Dad promised to accompany me to the orchard sett after dinner on Sunday to save the badgers but a surfeit of guinness and pork clubbed him unconscious. He lay snoring in the armchair while his stockinged feet cooked on the fender. Before the booze had silenced him he had sung his protest song:

> "The Working Class can kiss my ass,
> I've got a foreman's job at last"

to the traditional tune of Tannenbaum. And Mam had looked at him as if he had just shot Bambi, totally unamused and thoroughly socialist. Her party loyalty never faltered but he voted optimistically for the new King Arthur, irrespective of political colouration. Mam was concerned for the dignity of labour because she recalled the barbarism doled out to the Welsh miners in the strikes of the Twenties.

I thought of the Welsh grandfather I had seen only once sitting before the fire in his council house, lips purpled by heart disease. His kind trod the socialist blood trails – mine, pub, corner shop, home, the chapel perhaps, and the cemetery. In the Rhondda Valley great uncles spoke of the marches, the Red Flag and the singing. "Mai hen wlad fy nadau." Black South Wales of working class nobility and brute misery. And the terraces dominated by the homes of the captains of industry – great houses whose bricks were held together by my forefathers' sweat. Visions of hard men hewing Welsh steam coal. "Gas explosions, terrible funerals, whole villages of widows and orphans," Mam sobbed. Old men, bleeding coal from the slag heaps, choking on the smoking dust while the first race at Ascot produced genteel applause and Harrods bulged at the seams with spendthrift drones.

"O yes," Mam said. "O yes. Don't you forget, Brian. Don't you forget."

She also told me how they brought the ponies up out of the pits for the annual holidays. The animals enjoyed a fortnight in the sun before darkness reclaimed them.

"This one was called Gomer and there was Pal and there was Tam and there . . . and there. . . ."

The diggers were busy when I arrived at the sett. An afternoon of heavy showers had not dampened their enthusiasm. I knew them all – Fred Stone, Parry, Pinky the rag-and-boneman, Fred Endacott who sold Brixham fish from his pony cart, Wilf Diamond the rat catcher and Mr Tozer the second-hand shop proprietor of lower Winner Street. Tozer was portly, bald-headed, tight-lipped and beaked like a turtle. He was also a fund of wet sayings:

"Enough to freeze the wotsits off a brass thingummy."

Mam detested him, recognizing, I suppose, the predatory homosexuality which caused such a scandal at the St Ignatius Youth Club in the Fifties.

The brambles had been cleared from the entrances to the sett and the terrier put down the main hole had barked incessantly to tell the men the badgers were at home. Another Jack Russell was sent into the galleries and his yelping guided the picks, iron bars and mattocks, the shovels and spades. The bank was stony beneath its crust of red soil but not like a moorland hedge and the work gang made good progress.

Tied to a nearby hawthorn the three rough-haired and four smooth Jack Russells yapped and whined and tugged at their leashes. Mr Tozer waddled round them in his corduroys and hobnails, making slow downward movements with his outstretched hands and wheezing small-talk.

"There, there, there," he panted. "Bide still ma boodies. Us'll have they old brocks, yaas. Bide still. Us will. Us will."

Farmer Bickford and Tony joined the party. The farmer told Wilf Diamond about the damage the badgers had done to the corn, and the lie was swallowed eagerly by the "sportsmen". It lent respectability to the ritual.

Clouds piled above the western hills and rain slanted across the sun to form a bow that curved from Roundham Head to Broadsands. Across the grunts of the men and the clang of the metal on stone the hedgetop thorns creaked and whispered. Light twinkled on the ivy leaves and Mr Tozer's wet head. The sour reek of b.o. and unwashed clothes lifted from the knot of workers, and I wondered how the badgers were reacting. I could feel their terror rising from the ground in cold vibrations. Rain trickled down my neck as the shower hissed hard and passed on towards Paignton, dark and towering.

"We'm through," Fred Stone gasped.

A muddy Jack Russell backed out of the gallery and stood there snarling and bristling. The men's boots slipped in the mud and Parry crashed down on his arse and I gave him a swift V sign.

The rest of the terriers were released and swarmed around the collapsed entrance. Then the badger sow emerged ready for action and the dogs retreated but not before she had left her mark on a couple. Despite the blood and soil on the broad white stripe that ran down the centre of her face the badger was a handsome, bearlike creature. I got the impression of great strength in her grey body but the stumpy black legs didn't carry her very far. Diamond clouted her nose with an iron bar and she stopped and sneezed blood and the terriers flew at her, tearing and nipping until she recovered and slashed wildly to the right and left with her jaws.

I was to learn a few years later that it was not "proper" baiting. The iron badger clamp – the hideous tongs on long handles which pinned the animal to the ground before it was stunned – was not employed. Nor were the creatures chained and killed slowly by the sheer weight of numbers. This business was messier and haphazard but the worrying or badgering produced the desired result.

The men formed a half circle and drove her constantly into the pack of terriers, and the battle became noisy and savage. Blood, saliva, mud and badger excrement were whisked into a black gruel by the flailing feet. Rain fell unnoticed. Whenever the sow shook off the dogs and broke for freedom the spades and iron bars beat her back; and the baiting might have continued until the terriers were exhausted if Fred Endacott hadn't dealt the badger a blow on the neck with his mattock. For a moment the dogs fell back and the sow keeled over, silently, the blood pouring from her mouth and nose. The men kicked her casually just in case there was some fight left, then the dogs were allowed to finish the killing. Pigeons clapped out of the oak in the field next to Clennon Wood but she did not hear the din. Giddiness and nausea were dragging her irresistibly down into the darkness and the small eyes were misting.

"No use hittin' her on top of the head," Mr Tozer explained, mistaking my tenseness for excitement.

"Their heads is hard as stone. You got to go for the neck and spine. And mind they bliddy jaws. A man can lose his fingers in that mouth."

He dug his toe into the bleeding lump, proud of his work, proud of his Jack Russells who stood quivering over the carcass, the froth pink on their lips.

"They'm hellers," Fred Stone said. He was a thin, hawk-faced man wearing a paratrooper's beret and overalls.

"What you goin' to do with her?" I asked.

"Nothing. They'm vermin. They kills chickens and eats corn. If us didn dig 'em out they'd overrun the place like rats."

"Honest Fred?"

"On my wife's grave."

"But why don't you shoot them?"

"Tis the sport, boy – the diggin', workin' the dogs. What you cryin' about?"

"I idn. It's the rain."

The terriers drove the boar from the sett and he stood at bay, hackles raised and courageous despite his fear and misery. The dogs hesitated.

"Set to, set to," Tozer cried and he brought his iron bar down on the black and white muzzle. But the terriers were still fearful. The badger was tuned to a high pitch of response by his wild existence and fought off their attacks with awesome ferocity. The life in him was radiant but the men snuffed it out. A spade hacked his spine and he stumbled and grunted but would not fall. He dragged his stiff and useless hind legs and continued to savage the dogs as they flew at him.

"Put an end to it," said Farmer Bickford.

Fred Stone obediently delivered the coup de grace and life left the boar, noiselessly as it had left his mate, and his body was buried under a heap of dogs.

I watched everything, every small detail and felt anger, disgust and sickness give way to sadness. I was wet through and shivering but I wasn't crying. It was the sky weeping.

"If I was God," I wrote in my exercise book. "I'd take better care of my helpless wild animals."

Mr Greensleeves was puzzled and asked me to elaborate, so I told the class about the badger baiting and the headmaster who came from the Midlands was impressed. But Fred Stone's eldest son, Eric, sat arms folded, staring rigidly at the ceiling.

"They said the badgers didn feel anything," I cried. "But

they did. I mean, you tread on a dog's paw and he yells, and you tread on a cat's tail and he screams. So the badgers must have felt everything – the iron bars, the spades, the boots, the terriers' teeth. They were scared – I could see it. God's honour, Sir – I could see it."

"But how could you stand and watch?" asked Sonia Johnsie.

"I dunno. It didn seem real, none of it, like the things we saw in those films on Belsen."

Afterwards we discussed cruelty to animals – hunting, shooting and trapping living creatures for pleasure. Mr Greensleeves was a townee and a passionate blood sport abolitionist. He wrote on the blackboard in big white capitals: "To kill for pleasure is a sin."

Then he told us how prehistoric man's respect for other animals grew out of his knowledge of their strength and his own limitations and weaknesses. The wolves, lions, tigers and bears were rivals in the survival business but once man gained control of his environment he relapsed into pettiness, arrogance and cruelty. Mr Greensleeves gave us simplistic half-truths and we were close enough to the cave to accept them.

*   *   *

Sitting by the fireside I was inconsolable.

"They're among the stars, now, and happy," Mam said, cupping my face in her hands.

"They're lying in the mud," I whispered.

"The animal part of them, yes – but not their spirits, those lights you saw behind their eyes."

"Gone to God's halo," I said mysteriously.

"Don't fret no more, Bri. You can't keep suffering for every bird and animal. You won't have any heart left."

I read a poem in one of the country magazines Dad picked up on the dump. It was a sort of posh plea to keep alive old blood sport traditions and ended with the following lines:

> "Yet if once we efface the joys of the chase
> From the land and out-root the stud,
> Goodbye to the Anglo-Saxon race,
> Farewell to the Norman blood."

And I saw again the look on Parry's face when Fred Stone

struck the mortally wounded badger. And I recalled the dreadful arrogance of the woman on the horse who had ordered me to open the gate. But I wasn't crying. It was the sky weeping.

14
Craftsman and Labourer

There was ravishing beauty cupped by Clennon's hills and it spoke entirely to the emotions like the Elgar music but was open to countless interpretations. The same autumn morning could uplift me and sadden Mam and fill the shires with more than their usual share of peacefulness. So many experiences waylaid my senses: the drift and swirl of beech leaves; the silent dance of sea mist; tree blurred white by hoar frost standing motionless in a grey sky; the long smoking curl, crumble and crash of waves on a beach; stooked oats on a hillside above a blue sea. A horse could feel the splendour of the living world and I was still close to the animal state yet capable of elbowing hard at the trough of vice with the lowest adult. This is the paradox of the human condition – the recognition of glory around us as we slide willingly into spiritual squalor.

But O God how I loved those first hot brushes with sex. I loitered by the girls' lavatory at Jubilee Street Primary and waited for the ten-year-old vamps to drag me inside. Accompanied by four or five other willing, panting prisoners I would be forced to watch Doreen Harris stand knickerless on the lav seat, lifting her frock to give us a flash of what looked like a little brown mouse nestling under her belly where her thighs met. Alas, Miss Gilcrest nabbed us frozen there, gawking like

chocolate frogs and Mr Greensleeves applied the bamboo en-
thusiastically to beat the demons out of our bums. But Doreen
and Big Beryl flaunted their charms after school in the bombed
house by the Sands Road level crossing and a select band of boys,
including myself, were permitted to enjoy a clumsy demonstration of what sex could offer. I stood, knees knocking, while
Colin Yeo made several unsuccessful attempts to do what Mr
Gowman's rooster did so well and so regularly on top of the hens.
Ignorance preserved our innocence.

At 6.45 everyone except me rushed home to listen to *Dick
Barton, Special Agent* on the wireless. Neither of my parents
liked the programme. Dad thought it plain bloody daft and Mam
saw it as part of the self-perpetuating myth of public school
leadership and heroism. Night after night the lah-di-dah sleuth
and his servile lower-class yes men hunted down criminal
"master" minds of incredible stupidity. Dick's assistants-cum-
menials, Jock and Snowy, were ever-ready to change a tyre or
walk the dog or rough up the lesser villains while Dick made sure
everything remained "jolly sporting". He was a patronizing
establishment goodie like the vicar, the doctor, the magistrate,
the retired squadron leader turned market gardener, and so on
and so on. The voice of authority was very Noel Coward. It was
hilarious to hear it commentating on a football match for Pathe
News.

". . . end Methews collects a pass from Mortenson, sweeps
down the wing to send a couple of Austrian cheps the wrong way
before cent'ring pahfectly for Finney to score with his left foot."

Like sprinkling champagne on chips.

I enjoyed *Toy Town* but the wireless music disappointed me.
Twiddling the knob I would occasionally gatecrash a soirée of
chamber music and German lieder. People suffering under such
names as Toby Bottle and Amarantha Twench sawed frenetic-
ally away at violins and cellos, and inevitably there would be a
baritone called Coventry Bliss warbling something roguish and
camp.

Mam would snap off the set growling:

"Daft bloody pansy boy. God Almighty! Why do people pretend they can appreciate that noise?"

Her prejudices were too outrageous to be harmful, and in any
case I never took to the wireless. I preferred books although the
Mabinogion proved a disappointment and a puzzle. Apparently

Mam had been translating it into a language I could understand, exhibiting a raw, native talent for story telling. She had glossed it with her own magic and the unadulterated product seemed dull and stilted.

Being an only child I had the undivided attention of both my parents. Mam had been spared the harassment of a large family, and if I had had five or six brothers and sisters there would have been no encouragement to read or create. Miraculous things emerged from my broadening horizons but I discovered too how jealousy can sour the sweetest summer morning and how pain can warp the loveliest of visions. What is mean within us can dull that which lies beyond us. Yet the stream was colour and light flowing through thought and feeling; the overture of eternity. And Dad told me how a line of Shakespeare's verse stood forever beyond the reach of death's bony fist. So I built my poems religiously like the caveman artist, trying to bequeath immortality to the shires and the foxes and the badgers, placing them within tall hedges of words which the flail mowers of the future would never multilate.

*   *   *

The year closed sombrely, lit by pale, guttering larches. I had measles on bonfire night and mumps for Christmas; but the dog I prayed for remained a dream. Princess Elizabeth got married and Mam said it was another mouth for us to feed. We had shin of beef stewed on the night of the Royal Wedding, and Dad toasted the royal couple in best cider. "One day it will be Queen Elizabeth," he proclaimed. "Then everything will go right for England again."

Whenever emotion swamped my parents they surrendered to it and sailed out of themselves. Moderation and constraint were strangers in our home. Life lit the fuse and they went off like rockets.

"Fred Stone's put the price of rabbits up by threepence," Mam said. Beating meat rationing was more important than enthusing over royal weddings, and we did it by dealing with Tacker and Stone. Mam used Tacker who used everyone and everything else. He was nasty but necessary and Mam was in the survival business.

I still liked Tacker and he continued to fascinate me. He was by nature more Irish than English, giving himself recklessly to drink and life. For all his failings he was a creature not a stiff-upper-lipped puppet pumping out clichés and inanities, like your common or garden Victorian country gent. And he was a predator killing obsessively and coldly but he was not a hypocrite of the kind that eats veal and attacks fox hunting.

Nor was he a phony like the university don who drives a Porsche and has a flat on the campus and a weekend country cottage, and eats wholefoods and vomits Marxism. Tacker loved wholefoods, too – whole chickens, whole ducks, whole sheep's heads, whole legs of pork.

Walking down Stuggy Lane through the soft, cold fabric of late afternoon I was happy. Mumps had left me groggy but 1948 came in mild with primroses in the gardens of Paignton and pigeons crooning on Mrs Williams' roof. Tacker and Parry ambled ahead and became vague, giant shapes in the mist. All sound was muffled, then an oak tree came at me from the gloom, spreading its branches wide like a wrestler's arms.

We went into the meadow and emptied the snares. The rabbit danced wildly in the wire that was abruptly checking each leap. Tacker knelt and silenced it with the edge of his hand. Ladyship yikkered and nosed at the pocket flap of his great coat.

"Lil heller," Tacker grinned. "Tidn your turn. Bloodythirsty sod idn her?"

Parry nodded and fished out his tobacco tin. Both men had drunk heavily at Newton Abbot market and everytime they opened their mouths cider fumes fouled the air.

"Have a stogie, Tack," Parry said.

The hand-rolled cigarette was accepted and tapped on a thumbnail.

"I lost that nail back-along," said Tacker, struggling to keep his balance as he retrieved another rabbit.

"Got un ripped off by an alsation, lost a lot of flesh too."

"How did it happen, Tacker?" I asked.

"The dog was guardin' some bugger's fowls. But losing that nail saved my life."

Parry shook his head and thumbed a petrol lighter and frowned. Behind him the hills were visible now as dark lumps.

"True as true," said Tacker. "Soon as they gets me to hospital they sees I've got gum disease and tis rottin' me guts. So they do's up my hand and whips out me teeth – awl for free."

"It is amazin' what they can do these days," said Parry.

The wires yielded five rabbits and Tacker was glowing when we left the meadow. The creatures had been in the traps since the previous day but I thought no more of them than I did of the pig that was slaughtered to provide the sausages I had eaten for breakfast.

"Rain's about," Tacker said. "Tis too bliddy still. Come on, Taff – if ort's in they gins I'll buy 'ee a pint in the Waterside."

We scrambled over the hedge and dropped into the lane. Old season leaves rustled underfoot and I scuffed them up as I walked. Parry panted under the weight of the sackload of wires, nets, pegs, gins, hammers and rabbit carcases. Tacker made him carry the gear to establish the difference in status between mere labourer and craftsman. I grinned at the little Welsh man.

"Don't your Mam mind you being out all hours of the day and night, Carter?" he grunted.

"Not during the holidays."

"Christ! – you're only ten. It is not normal the way you run round like a stray dog."

"Mind his Dad don't hear 'ee say that," said Tacker. "I'd think twice about rubbin' Perce up the wrong way."

"Well, the little bugger could offer to carry something."

"He's lookin' out for pheasants and things. He'm sharp as a fox. If you cut the yap maybe you'd be more use than a donkey."

"Car-ark," cried the crows, flapping into the top of the tallest elm, well out of gunshot.

"Us've got something," Tacker said.

"Duck?" said Parry.

I unlatched the gate at the end of the lane. The gins had been tilled under water in the shallows under the fringe of the marsh.

"Looks like a bliddy girt goose," cried Tacker, breaking into a run.

I knew what it was and followed him with less enthusiasm.

"Bliddy old owull," Tacker bellowed. "Bliddy awld owull. What's 'er doing in a gin?"

There was a lambency of feathers in the mud. The bird opened and closed its wings, showing lustrous white, then gold-dappled honey. It was a moment of almost supernatural beauty beneath the gathering rain gloom.

Beside the owl lay the partly submerged body of a jack snipe and I could picture what had happened. Hunting the margins of the dump through yesterday's dusk the owl had seen the flash of the snipe's wings where the little wader tried frantically to lift free of the serrated iron jaws that held its legs. Down dropped the barn owl to take the snipe only for another trap to snap shut on her left leg. From mounting horror I imagined what the creatures had endured through the long hours of darkness and I heard their cries mingling with the rabbits' screams. Even though the rabbits' terror made me feel sick I could tell myself they were destined for the table and if I didn't get them the fox or the buzzard would grab them. But to trap an owl whose beauty had haunted me for three winters seemed utterly base. Many emotions met in confusion around my heart.

"You can't kill it, Tacker," I said. "No one kills owls. Give it to me and I'll make it better. For Chrissake, Tacker. It's bad luck to kill owls. Give it to me."

He handled the bird gently and looked up, caught my eye and dropped his head again and said: "Hold her, boy."

The owl quivered under my fingers and clacked her mandibles, reminding me suddenly and insanely of Grandad quibbling his dentures. For an awful moment I teetered on the brink of laughter but somehow I controlled myself.

"Easy, ma 'ansome," Tacker whispered. He pressed down with his foot and the gin gaped and we saw the owl's ruined leg. Before he could utter a word I jumped in.

"I can mend it, Tacker," I said, reading his mind. "Honest. I'm good with birds and things. And I won't let on where it came from."

"What you got there, Carter?" Parry cried from the gateway.

"Bliddy awld owull," Tacker said. "The bugger's scared off the duck."

The barn owl pressed against me.

"I told you it was a waste of time putting gins in the marsh," Parry sneered. "Funny bloody duck, that one."

"Shut your gob and give us the sack," said Tacker. "You let the auld owull bide in there, Bri," he added with surprising tenderness.

"Look at its leg, man!" mewled Parry. "No one'll buy that rubbish. Best bash it on the head now and put it out of its misery."

"Open the sack, you crabby lil bugger," Tacker roared and he waved a fist under Parry's nose.

"No offence, Tacker. No offence."

The owl was plunged into the rabbity darkness of the sack and I took a deep breath and tried to grin.

Between banks of bullen and hazel the sheep had left their smell. A blackbird muscled through the tangled twigs and said spink! five times. At the end of the lane through the bars of the gate the watermeadows could be seen. Parry fiddled with the catch and the gate swung wide. We entered the meadow and Tacker was kneeling beside the run killing a snared rabbit when Farmer Bickford, Tony and Ernie stepped from the hedge.

"Up to your old tricks, Willock?" Bickford said.

"Seems like it, boy," Tacker smiled.

"Don't worry," said the farmer coldly. "Us seen 'ee take they rabbits in Oppy Meadow. You Willocks is all the same, worsn thievin' bliddy gypos."

Tacker set his jaw.

"I've phoned the police," Bickford continued. "You idn getting away with it this time."

"You'm awl wind and piss, boy," said Tacker. "You got to run to the law like an old maid."

"Doan 'ee sound off at me, Willock," said Bickford in a voice thick with anger. "I'm not havin' no bone idle sod of a poacher stealin' ort that belongs to me."

"You'm a bit late," Tacker grinned. "Ask your missus."

"That's enough," said Ernie, uncomfortably.

The first raindrops made dark blossoms on the hedgerow soil.

"I want that useless ornament put away," the farmer grated pointing his stick at Tacker.

"And who'll take care of your missus when I'm inside?" Tacker said.

The skin suddenly tightened on the cheekbones of Bickford's pale wedge of a face and the punch came up and over his shoulder like the arm action of a fast bowler. Tacker brushed it aside and rammed his knee into Bickford's groin. Then the great left fist went to work and the farm labourers were hard pressed to drag him off.

"I reckon you've cooked your own goose this time, Willock," Tony said. "Poaching's bad enough but assault is bloody serious."

He put his foot in a cowpat and nearly did the splits and I laughed. The sight of grown men fighting was like a scene from a Charlie Chaplin film.

"You're in the shit too, Carter," Tony said.

"He's got nothing to do with it," said Tacker jerking free and crouching ready for more trouble.

"You can't punch your way out of this, Tacker," said Ernie. "Go home, man, now – before the police get here."

"They know the way to your door, Willock," Bickford said. "And every blow you struck is goin' to cost 'ee a month of your freedom. Mark my words."

"I only carried the sack and did what he told me," whined Parry. "I thought he had permission, you see. When you're out of work with a wife and three kids to feed you'll do anything to earn a bob or two."

"Except get up in the morning," said Tony. "No use settin' snares on private property if you idn going to visit them before sunrise, boy. Us have been hanging round Oppy Meadow since Mrs Brinham saw the rabbits in your wires. Christ, you'm more mazed than you look!"

Tacker narrowed his eyes and spat.

"The kid's not involved," he said. "He tagged along for the walk. Us couldn't get rid of un."

"Is that true?" the farmer asked me.

I nodded and said innocently: "Idn you allowed to catch rabbits in Clennon, Mr Bickford?"

"Not on my land, no sir – no bliddy poacher takes my rabbits."

He leaned on his stick and tried to patch up his bruised dignity. Three red lumps had appeared on his face and his lower lip was split.

"I'd bet money on you and your mate going down for a long time, Willock," he added quietly.

"O my God. O my God," Parry gasped. "What sort of mess have you got me in, Willock? My wife will kill me when she finds out."

"If you doan stop catterwaulin, I'll break your bliddy neck," Tacker snarled.

"Your breaking days are over, Willock," said the farmer. "Tip up that sack, Ern, and let's see how many of my amimals they got."

The trapping gear, the rabbit carcasses and an odd, buff-coloured 'parcel' of feathers tumbled out.

"You sods," Ernie said and it was the first time I had heard him swear.

"A barn owl," Farmer Bickford said contemptuously.

"Us caught un by mistake," said Tacker.

"In a gin he tilled for duck down on the marsh," Parry said.

"Is it dead?" asked Tony.

"No, but it should be," said Parry. "It's leg is all crushed."

Ernie crouched over the bird and was briefly caught up in the flash of feathers. The blunt pinions beat desperately but only for the second the owl needed to launch itself skywards. And it was gone, flapping over the valley through the rain that came from the Atlantic. Humans were forgotten as it pursued something small and living along the edge of a gut and pounced only to be betrayed by its dead leg. But it survived, and I discovered later that it was the hen bird. She returned to Broome Linhay and let her mate take care of her until the wound healed and she could grip prey with both feet again.

Tacker was imprisoned for six months and Parry was put on probation. All I got was a thick ear from Tony who resented the way I had pulled the wool over Farmer Bickford's eyes.

*   *   *

"Willock was a big dick," said O'Flaherty, patting the head of Billy the lurcher.

"My old gran could've stole a few rotten rabbits wivvout gettin' her collar felt."

"Your old gran," I snorted.

And the cigarette card left my hand at the flick of a wrist and skimmed the cobbles to land tight against the wall beyond all the other cards.

"Jammy bugger," O'Flaherty said but he let me gather up the cards I had won.

"How long you got the dog?" Colin said.

"He goes on Saturday," I said. "Mam won't keep him so Parry is goin' to look after him till Tacker comes out. The creep."

"Tacker will still beat him up, my dad says," Colin smiled.

"They'd razor slash him up in the smoke," said Horseshit. "That Parry is a right grass the way he talked in court."

We strolled up the terrace taking turns to throw the tennis ball for Billy to retrieve. Behind almost every door there was the sound of children's voices and smoke lofted from the chimneys, and the front steps were spotless.

15
What the Hedges Said

The winter of Forty-Seven was the 1812 overture, the grand slam of hard weather, and everything that followed seemed tame. Miss Millman, whose daily exercise was a snail-crawl to Penk's and back, no longer "tut-tutted" when confronted by a little cat ice on the cobbles. Birds whistled and sang and cats loped along the sandstone walls, pausing to sniff at the dead sticks of valerian before going about their business. Watching them from our front doorstep I discovered they were always purposefully on the move, treading the same territory and never simply mouching like the children that flew past the terrace in gangs.

By relating to animals and birds I began to see certain basic truths concerning myself and the world around me. I wasn't merely an element assembled with others to form the substance of a day. I was me, as the blackbird was blackbird and the cat was cat.

Between Candlemas and St Valentine's Day I searched Clennon for signs of an early spring, yearning now for greenness and warm sunlight. Recovering from an attack of bronchitis I strolled through a fine soft morning into the watermeadows. The hills were draped with the thinnest of mists and the gulls wheeled white and silent above the rubbish dump. Everywhere I looked I found signs of returning life. The first small leaves of bramble and elderberry were uncurling in the hedges and on the fringe of the reed beds I saw at my feet two celandines – one open, one closed. Soon the grass bordering the cattlepath would blaze with the little golden flowers and the kestrel tacking low across the sky would see minute points of brilliance all down the valley.

Up on Broome Park I scattered half-a-dozen rabbits and flushed a green woodpecker from the trees behind the ricks. The bird fell and undulated away, its laugh rattling behind it.

"What do you know, Carter?" Midge said sullenly.

"I saw a yaffle down Clennon this morning."

She held the gate open by less than three inches and peered through the gap so that only one eye, her nose and half her mouth were visible.

"Well?" she said.

"Is Tacker all right?"

"How do I bliddy know? He's up Exeter. I'm yer."

"He asked me to look after the ferrets."

"Sod off! You and 'im and they soddin' fitches."

'P.S. Is that old owull okay?' Tacker had written in his childish, rounded script on the prison notepaper. The rest of the letter was an unpunctuated plea to 'tend they ferrets'. But Midge wouldn't let me near them and everytime I tried to scale the wall of her yard at night she rushed out of the kitchen and threw things at me.

Rain fell hard for a week and at Clennon a heron fished where once the cattle had grazed. I waded the floodwater lake and climbed the hedge. The rain rattled on my sou'wester and snaked down my face. The heron who loved solitude glanced at me, cried "aarnk" and took to the air. I splashed across the meadow into the wind that tasted cold and muddy. Every so often the fury of the storm diminished and the countryside emerged stark and vibrating like a grey and dull green tapestry. But the wind never stopped worrying the great elms which roared and threshed around the linhay.

I ran inside the building and the volume of din was suddenly turned down. Lichens and harts tongue ferns braided the granite pillars and in the corner a mess of mutes and pellets betrayed the owls. I stood motionless while behind me the rain flapped and hissed, but the birds looking down from a gap between the top of the wall and the roof did not seem too upset.

"Don't go," I crooned. "No one's going to hurt you. No. No – you're perfect. Perfect."

The barn owls began to shift nervously and I wanted to tell them I was a go-between representing an inarticulate country-man who could not voice his remorse.

Next day I plucked up enough courage to return to the Willock house. Midge was struggling to get the key in the front door and she fixed me with the unblinking malice of her little piggy eyes and growled:

"Get lost, Carter."

"Are the ferrets OK, Midge?"

"They'm better off than me."

Her coat was thrust out by the lump of newly minted life in her belly.

"Yes – I'm in the club, Carter."

I didn't know what to say so I shook my head and scratched around for meaningful words.

"Is – is Ladyship getting enough exercise, Midge?"

"Sod off, snothead, before I kill you. Go on. Leave me be-ee-ee."

Her voice rose to a scream and I galloped up the street as windows went up and doors opened.

"Poor maid," Dad said at the tea table. Firelight twinkled along the brass fender and the backroom was alive with warmth.

"Who's the father?" Mam said. "Who the hell would want that for a bit on the side?"

Curled up in the armchair, I came to understand what a "bit-on-the-side" meant. "Bits-on-the-side" weren't proper people and they had no right to expect to be loved. They were objects to be used, rejected, ridiculed and condemned.

During a cold spell a couple of weeks later concern for the ferrets brought me again to Tacker's house.

" 'Er's over the pub," Mrs Smale next door told me. " 'Er's always up the pub. Tidn respectable round yer no more with him up there and 'er over yonder."

The back gate was banging in the wind that rattled the clothes line against the pole. I crossed the yard and my heart sank with every step. Two skeletons lay entwined in the hutch amongst dirty green and black scraps of fur.

Midge sat by the fire in the saloon bar of the Victoria and

Albert pouring a Mackeson into her grey face. She would carry that look of tired resignation to the grave.

"The ferrets are dead then, Midge," I said from the doorway. It was all I could dredge up from my misery.

She lit a cigarette and breathed smoke out on a sigh.

"You let them starve away. Christ! – Tacker will kill you. He loved Ladyship. How could you do it? How, Midge? Why?"

"Sod the ferrets. Sod Dad."

Midge picked at her teeth with a fingernail and said: "The babby's dead, too. It was born dead as if God was angry and killed 'er. A little girl babby. Dead as a stone."

"But –"

"Sod off, Carter. You and they bliddy fitches! What do you know about ort?"

The barman stuck his head through the serving hatch and barked at me. Rushing down Winner Street I clenched my teeth and spat obscenities. Dusk was the saddest time but as darkness gathered the street lamps flared and I ran on to the valley while the pain ebbed.

The evening was frosty and cattle lay in the white grass chewing the cud. I walked among them as far as the dead pine beside the stream. Then the thin, familiar cries drifted over the frozen flood pools and the barn owls came on their soft wings and darkness mantled all the things the heart could not endure. But I heard the past speaking to me in the whisper of the hedges. Some unfathomable grief had settled on the valley and all the dead creatures I had loved and those I had never known called out lest the mind strayed from remembering. So I sang the wordless song in the place full of yesterdays. O foxes. O badgers. O life that burns so strong in the brown hare.

Though the music still rises from the valley, the magic has fled and the heart of the hills is broken.

*   *   *

Hugging my knees and rocking backwards and forwards I stared into the fire. Mam was telling me about her girlhood spent beside the River Wye. Gritty gusts of rain hit the window and the washing flapped and cracked like a whip on the line. She spoke English but thought in Welsh and beneath the babble of the language we shared were the murmurings of a far older tongue.

Indeed Mam had the gift of the gab, stuffing plain English with a rich seasoning of Welsh vowel sounds and releasing it all in wild torrents of words. The light that radiated from her smile is the light that shines from eternal childhood and is replenished by successive generations of children. She never grew up and was therefore constantly amazed by the universe. Perhaps this is why she peppered her monologues with a peculiar and highly individual syntax. And when she lapsed into her native tongue I was treated to language full of the rapture of a Bach fugue.

But I leant towards the hill silence of Wordsworth whose eloquence was profound and totally English. He spoke a language for all seasons, the language of childlike astonishment. Spring brought the green bloom back to Clennon and Miss Lee read us 'Lucy Gray' and John Davidson's 'A Runnable Stag', and 'The Scarecrow' by Walter de la Mare. But the poet's scarecrow wasn't horrific enough for my liking so I wrote my own verse celebrating Bickford's manic-looking dawbake.

> *The Dawbake*
> Up in the turnip field old turnip head
> smiles at me for he isn't dead.
> On moonlit nights he creeps down
> across the marshes into town.
> The clock strikes two and three and four,
> and I hear him at my bedroom door.
> "Come out," he whispers, "come out to play."
> But I tell the dawbake to go away.
> And off he goes into the dark
> to eat the ducks of Elmsleigh Park.

"I shall take it with me to Australia," Miss Lee said, folding the poem and placing it carefully in her briefcase.

"Why are you going all that way, Miss?" asked Sonia Johnsie and I saw the tears bright under her lashes.

"It's a challenge," said Miss Lee. "Australia is the new world."

Doreen Harris caught my eye and sniffed.

"Do you have to go, Miss?" I said.

"Yes. Everything's arranged. All I want to do before I sail is win the Dancing Cup at the Festival."

Then her lower lip quivered and she opened the big cupboard in the corner and remained sorting through the art material far longer than usual. Things were coming to an end and we all felt it, even simple-minded Arthur Crocker whose disobedient sphincter muscle caused him nearly as much trouble as words and sums and anything vaguely intellectual.

In true, fairy-tale fashion we won the cup for Miss Lee and twenty-six children in my class passed to go on to Grammar or Technical Schools. But Butch Meredith and Soapy Tucker learnt they were to join O'Flaherty at the Secondary Modern. The news did not please Butch.

"The big boys will look after you," I said.

"Says you," Butch grumbled. "I wish I was brainy, Bri. Bloody hell, I wish I was."

"I don't," said Soapy, defiantly. "I want to go to Tween-away."

"The bloody little fool," Dad said when I reported this to him. "You work your arse off at grammar or you'll end up reading gas meters or swinging a pick. Old Wordsworth wouldn't have seen too much 'splendour in the grass' if he'd been humpin' coal off the Co-op cart."

He sipped his tea and pointed a finger at me.

"The moral is," he said, "if you've got anything to say get it on paper and up the neighbours and the bosses and worms like young Tucker. What they know about life and culture could be inscribed on a gnat's foreskin with a jack hammer."

"And whose fault is that?" cried Mam. "Who kept us ignorant and why? You great prawn."

The dishcloth sailed across the kitchen and draped itself round Dad's head and he made no effort to remove it.

"You look like Lawrence of Arabia," I laughed.

"The Sheik of bloody Arabi," Mam giggled.

*   *   *

Sportsday was the last great occasion in my primary school calendar. I had been selected to represent Jubilee Street Primary in the hop-step-and-jump and the relay at the inter-junior school athletics meeting at Queens Park. Mr Greensleeves kept telling us what a privilege it was to be wearing the dark blue band of Jubilee Street, but what he really meant was: "You are competing for me. You are products of my wonderful education system. So get out and bring back the laurels." I could not forget how he had curbed Arthur Crocker's enthusiasm during the preliminary competitions when we were running for a place in the squad.

It was customary to assemble in the hall and wait for Mr Greensleeves and three of the staff to march us down to the park. Crocker was bouncing about like a Mexican bean in his massive black daps.

"I bet I'm first in the hundred yards," he crowed.

"How much?" asked Butch, scenting profit.

"Ninepence."

"A bob," said Butch, and they shook hands.

"Were you talking, Crocker?" roared Mr Greensleeves.

"No Sir – I mean, yes Sir – I mean – I mean. . . ."

"Stay behind and practise being quiet for an hour or two," Mr Greensleeves said amiably from the rostrum. "The rest of you, single file into the playground."

"But Sir," bleated Crocker. "I got new daps."

"And they'll remain new if you keep opening your mouth," the headmaster smiled.

Tears flowed freely down Crocker's fat cheeks and his chin dropped onto his chest. Miss Lee spoke quietly to Mr Greensleeves but he shook his head and I heard the words "discipline" and "self-control". Then Crocker evacuated his bowels and the stench cleared the floor around him. He was led, stiff-legged and sobbing to the toilets but not before Butch had reminded him of the bob bet.

Our relay team was placed second in the final but I came nowhere in my individual event although I had bettered the winning distance by two feet in practice.

"You'll have to pull up your socks at Grammar School," Mr Greensleeves said irritably. "What on earth happened?"

"Dunno, Sir."

"It didn't look as if you were trying? Were you trying, Carter?"

I shrugged and said: "Sort of, Sir."

"Sort of!" he fumed. "Sort of? 'Sort of' isn't good enough, Carter. Not good enough. What did you have, lad – a moral blackout? Did you funk-out?"

I shrugged and stared down at my gym shoes.

"Well," he said in a voice that trembled with disbelief. "I think I understand. O yes – I understand. Be in my study tomorrow morning. And rest assured – this will go on your report."

But my Night Terrors mysteriously returned and I missed the last week of term, and Mr Greensleeves had to content himself with a letter to my parents.

Dad opened it and read it secretly in the lavatory.

"Is it true?" he said.

"A bit, yes. Greensleeves is like Old Man Forsey. He was rotten to that looby Arthur Crocker. Anyway why do you have to keep on coming first?"

"I don't," he smiled.

"You goin' to tell Mam, Dad?"

"No," he said. "I put the letter down the pan and pulled the chain."

16
Grammar School

The summer had a muted Alice in Wonderland quality of time in confusion. Mam took visitors with strange northern accents and gave them bed and breakfast and evening meals as well as providing for our needs. This enabled her to buy my school uniform – the grey suit with short trousers, grey stockings, new black shoes, the navy blue and red striped tie and the breast pocket badge, the navy blue cap and new navy gabardine raincoat. Standing in front of the mirror looking like something off the Harrow shelf I might have wondered where Mam's socialism ended and her secret ambitions began. But I didn't think of anything except the school that drew closer each day while Greensleeves receded into the past like a figure glimpsed from the window of a moving train.

Miss Lee departed and I never saw her again although she constantly came to mind. Her goodness endured and her encouragement kept me writing and drawing and believing in my small, personal vision.

The fair visited Paignton Green and Mam took me all dressed up in cap and suit, showing me off as an example of homespun scholastic success. And I felt silly and hot and avoided Butch and the others. Brutally the primary school world collapsed before I realized how precious those days were at Jubilee Street.

*   *   *

August of the crowded town and beaches, of burning sun and
dark thunder clouds was particularly exciting for me and Colin.
Butch had drifted closer to Soapy and the rest of the embryo
secondary modern boys who were herding together for the long
tramp up Totnes Road to Tweenaway School. Gang life persisted
but I sensed the resentment and suspicion. Every now and then
O'Flaherty's sneering face registered the emotions Butch and
Co. struggled to conceal.

"Right effin lah-di-dah, aintcha," he mocked.

Colin's big ears stuck out like taxi doors left open and Horseshit gripped them and twisted them in his fingers. For some
inexplicable reason those ears irritated me and I couldn't raise
any sympathy for Colin and secretly enjoyed his humiliation.

"Bloody snot-noses, you and Carter. Wotcherfinkyar? – toffs?
A couple of posh, stuck-up dicks?"

The gang's laughter struck me as something pagan and
dangerous, echoes of the ritual of weeding out abnormals from
primitive societies. But Mam said the other kids would get used
to it and come round in the end when they realized we hadn't
changed. She was partly right. Education distanced us from
them as our interests took different roads and their limitations
became more and more apparent.

On very hot days we romped barefoot to Goodrington and
dived for coins from the promenade. The tourists, who were
known locally as visitors, were only too willing to chuck
tanners and bobs and even the odd half-crown into the gin clear
sea at high tide. Fifteen foot of water sucked and gurgled round
the steps where the pleasure boats collected trippers for an
hour's mackerel fishing. The coin glittered and wobbled down
through the shafts of sunlight towards the green perpetual
gloom of the seabed. I could dive deeper than the others and
lurked below their tangled bodies waiting to grab the silver
piece before it was lost in the weed.

Another profitable business venture was 'lifting' mackerel.
When the shoals came with the spring tides and hunted the
herring fry along the margins of Torbay the visitors crowded
Goodrington Prom and dropped their lines and hauled in fish by
the job lot. The crowd of fishermen and spectators hung over the
handrails watching the flash and shimmer of the packs driving

hard into the great silver drifts of fry. Colin, Butch, Horseshit and I lurked behind the action where the dead mackerel were piled. Then we nipped from heap to heap, snatching one here, a couple there and stuffing them in the old sackcloth frail I was carrying. This way we acquired enough to sell and enough for a share-out. Only once did our filching come unstuck. A beady teenage girl spotted me stealing a brace of her dad's fish and came after me like a rat out of a burning brewery. She had long legs and caught me halfway up the rock-walk. I cowered against the samphire while she emptied the evidence onto the path.

"You," she said. "Are a thief."

"The fish belong to everyone, Miss. They come out of the sea. Tidn stealing."

"Did you catch them?"

My head dropped and I made no reply.

"Well?"

"Us don't get a lot to eat, Miss."

Her tone softened.

"Are you hungry?"

"Yes, Miss – me and me brothers and sisters."

"How many brothers and sisters have you got?"

"Four, Miss."

"Four of each!"

"No – two brothers and two sisters. Dad got killed in the war."

"Pick up the fish," she said. "And put them back in the bag."

"Idn you goin' to tell the police?" I said, catching her eye.

"No. But if there's a next time I will."

"Can I keep the mackerel, Miss."

"Yes. Go on, go."

But tramping up the sun-dappled path to the pines I felt dirty inside.

"Silly cow," Butch said, parting the bushes and joining me.

"She wasn't," I said.

"She let you go, didn she?" he said scornfully.

I grabbed a mackerel from the bag and held it under his nose.

"How would you like this stuck up your bum?" I growled.

"What have I done?" he protested. "Tell me what I've done."

"You're a turd."

"OK, I'm a turd."

Looking at him I saw Tacker standing there making a victory

out of something he would never understand.

Mrs Meredith was a working-class entrepreneur and all of her children were productive, adding their shillings and pence to the family budget. Brenda had a paper round, Johnny was a telegraph boy and Butch worked for Mr Matthews the butcher every Saturday morning. All the brood beavered away to create an atmosphere of total industry and the Meredith house was one of the happiest in our terrace.

I think Mrs Meredith hit on the idea of transferring Butch from the Baptist Church to Anglican St Wilfred's where novice choir boys received five-and-six a month. Butch made a corn-crake sound musical but he collected his silver every fourth Wednesday at choir practice. For him God was a foggy King Kong-like spectre you encountered in old age. All the rest was bullshit you endured to ward off thunderbolts and plagues. But his anarchistic impulses withered at the vestry doors and he was the only choirboy who refused to fart during the sermon. He sat grimly on his wind, nursing visions of retribution while we warbled and trilled blasphemously into our cassocks.

I was a member of St Wilfred's choir for exactly one calendar month, having pinned my faith to the five-and-six. Unfortunately Colin and Soapy were equally bored by the incense swinging and the incantations and the deadly seriousness of rubbing shoulders with the Christian God.

"God's a kind of grey old dick," Colin said, heaving off his surplice. We had been rehearsing for the Harvest Festival service and the balmy night was divinely alive with bats.

"Let's go to Old Man Forsey's," I said, conveying the Devil's message.

"The pixie," Butch grinned.

I carried him on the drop handlebars of my Raleigh three-speed sports bike which my eleven-plus performance and a Co-op endowment policy had brought into my life. We used the bicycle as a climbing frame to get onto the wall under the pear tree. The pixie was in its familiar position beside the pond, gazing blindly across the lily pads. From behind the orange glow of the closed curtains came the strains of a Strauss waltz.

"Up the tree?" Colin whispered.

"No – I've a better idea," I said.

So the pixie was kidnapped and hidden in the cellar of the bombed house by the Sands Road level crossing. A brief visit from PC Tarr failed to break me and the Forseys were left to ponder the mystery. But not for long.

The summer holidays were nearly over. They closed with a heat wave and the screaming of swifts went on late into the night. The sky was crowded with small black scimitars weaving their patterns over the stars. Passing through the Parish church-yard I would see them high up on the red Norman tower, cling-ing to the side of the man-made cliffs. And they would hawk the air above Dancing Fox Marsh taking hoverflies and spiders by the thousand, preparing for the hazardous journey to the pyra-mids. They were great travellers and I felt privileged to stand in the sky on Cider Mill Hill among them. Nothing filled me with so much exultation as the hilltop on a calm September evening watching the massed dance of the swifts. All about me the green and tawny farmland paced into mist. If I lay face down I would glimpse the spitting spider gobbing sticky thread on some minute insect, and overhead the buzzards angled their wings against the sea breeze. At the centre of creation the gong of life was struck and the vibrations carried to the ends of the universe. Gulls lifting from the surf, cattle sounding their warhorns in the meadows and hares in the corn. Then the red of hips and haws and the gold and crimson and scarlet of apples all down the coombe from the cider mill to Stuggy Lane.

Going to grammar school wouldn't change a thing. I still had the valley which the rhythms of the seasons played upon, and Bathsheba would always be there to wreath me in the glory of her mane.

*   *   *

Colin Yeo's big brother Eric was fifteen and in his school certi-ficate year. He was another of those peripheral figures that rarely appeared on the terrace scene but his influence was con-siderable and he was a street fighter with a mean reputation. Furthermore he was the scourge of O'Flaherty and gave the cockney a hard time whenever their paths crossed.

"We're in Eric's horsebox," Colin said.

He lolled self-consciously against our draining board and watched Mam parting my hair before she applied the face flannel to the egg round my lips.

Our suits and caps were so new we could not bear to meet

anyone en route to the train. We sneaked down the back lanes until we were safely on Paignton Station with the other "sprogs" as the new boys were called.

The prairie tanker puffed in from Kingswear and Colin guided me to the rear of the train and the grammar school horseboxes. These were compartments without linking corridors – big, roomy cells stinking of sour upholstery, carbolic soap, brylcream and tobacco smoke.

I hesitated before stepping up.

"Don't be shy, piglet," said a mirthless voice. "Come into my parlour."

Colin and the wretched Clarke Herbert followed me into the horsebox and the steam hissed and the door slammed behind us. Five dark shapes stirred and the glowing tips of five cigarettes traced red circles in the gloom. All the blinds were down until the bulky figure in a far corner released one of them and daylight streamed dramatically in to give me my first glimpse of Messrs Hodgeson, Bullock, Prout and Slocombe. Eric, I knew, but not as the leader of the fifth form welcoming committee.

"Carter, Herbert and my turd of a brother – Dumbo," he said, waving a hand like a dead whiting. "Observe Dumbo's ears, gentlemen. Most peculiar phenomena."

"Quite so," wheezed the heavy Hodgeson.

"Herr . . . Bert," he added pensively. "It has a teutonic ring. Herr Adolf Bert?"

"Clarke Herbert," Herbert snapped. "I'm not a bliddy German."

Knuckles flashed and beat a savage tattoo on his skull.

"You are what we say you are," said Eric Yeo.

"Hapless, hideous Herbert."

"Horrid Herbert", in an asthmatic whisper.

"Horntoad Herbert," Bullock smiled.

"Herbert the haemorrhoid," said Prout.

"Herbert halitosis," Slocombe said.

And they gathered round the cowering sprog and beat his head with the peaks of their caps until he whimpered. Colin and I sat quietly alert, hoping the novelty of Herbert would prevail until the train reached Torre.

"It's worse on the way home," a second year informed me as we walked up the hill to the venerable seat of learning. Torquay Grammar School was a tall, wide, grey building holding the gleam of its windows to the sky. It soared above the shrubberies at the top of a drive that wound past the lawn tennis courts, a dilapidated annexe and a collection of wooden shacks. Herbert galloped into form 1A and Colin and I found ourselves in a shack with 1B stencilled on the door.

The hut stood behind a little spinney of scrub elm and conifers where pigeons crooned and I caught a glimpse of magpies. Our form-master and religious instruction teacher was the saintly young Mr Johnson, nicknamed Chick because of his gentleness and amiable disposition. Apart from proving to be one of the best human beings I've ever known Chick loved natural history and literature and was to prove the spur in my literary endeavours.

Up at the main school of echoing corridors and silent classes of scholars hunched over their desks like medieval monks, I met Mr Jones the art master who would soon be revealing sumptuous new vistas for my imagination to patrol. He would introduce me to the Renaissance giants and the quiet seers of wildlife art like Archibald Thorburn. I also encountered the lower school maths expert nicknamed Skull for obvious reasons. Under him any interest I had in numbers, algebraic symbols, circles, angles and squares faded into a fog of incomprehension. He would mumble and splutter through his lessons leaving a trail of baffled casualties in his wake, creating a new generation of the mathematically tone deaf.

Recalling the more flamboyant and eccentric members of staff is easy: Mousy Martin, the senior French master; "DER" – the huge, bald geography master with his habit of leaning on his desk and pumping two or three "ders" into every sentence he uttered.

"The River Thames meanders – der – across rich alluvial plains – der – to – der – the sea."

Greek was the province of a sexy young lady called Miss Roper who was the subject of outrageous rumours, lies and mythology. "Would plump Miss Roper let me groper," demanded the wistful graffiti on the lavatory wall next to "God is dead – but don't worry, Mary's in the club again".

Mr Kneebone taught history and Snoop forced Latin verbs into us and a cynical ex-fighter pilot offered basic Spanish. A host of masters and a few mistresses flapped in and out of my new school life in their black gowns. Presiding over the flock was "Joe" Harmer, un upright Christian of a headmaster, cast in the Matthew Arnold mould but rather lacking Arnold's warm humanity. I was soon to discover he could cane harder and more accurately than Greensleeves. Undoubtedly he was a good man but he made no real impact on my grammar school years.

The first day was a slow motion trip through a haze. Big anonymous shapes blundered into my knowing and dispensed information or kindness or misery according to their nature. Herbert fared badly because he over-reacted to the things that went on in the horsebox. He had been denied the advantage of a long apprenticeship to pain under the expert tuition of Horseshit O'Flaherty. But it was hard to feel sympathy for the moist-eyed toad, remembering his past betrayals and odious playground activities. Luckily we had an advocate in Eric and almost welcomed the initiation ceremony as the young Zulu must have welcomed his duel with the lion.

The brief period of bullying sent Clarke scuttling off to a softer horsebox. His balls had been blacked with boot polish and Hodgson had sat on his head and farted, and Prout had twanged his toggle with an elastic band. So he skulked off and was absorbed into the porridgy mess of lower form insect life never to be noted again.

"Look at your cap," Mam said. "God, boy! – have you been playin' football with it?"

"It fell under the train."

"Just like that! Off your nut and under the wheels."

She planted a splathering kiss on the top of my head and clutched me to her thin, bony body. Her eyes were on me but she was looking into her girlhood again and treading the happy places.

"O," she breathed. "There's lucky you are, Brian. You will work hard for your Mam, won't you? Don't waste a moment."

And I knew she was holding Dr Carter, the King's physician, or Professor Carter the brain surgeon or Briano von Karter, the conductor of the Boston Symphony Orchestra, or Jesus Carter, the saviour of the Welsh working class. I was her future and she held all her dreams and longings in her arms.

"Yes – yes, you'll get on for your Mam."

How wonderful were the weekends now after five schooldays and five evenings of homework. Bright cascades of light fell through the cider apple trees and the leaves of Mortimer's horse

chestnuts were rust-red at the edges. Peacock butterflies robed
the buddleia of the Sands Road bomb site and heavy dews
lingered all day in the orchards. Colin, Butch and I cycled to
Dittisham and picked plums but the comradeship had died and
the bonhomie was false. Mrs Meredith fell out with Mam and
doors which seemed to have been open all my life were suddenly
slammed in my face. The Harvest Festival fiasco did not help.

Miss Butterworth who supervised the Sunday School was
agreeably surprised when Butch, Colin and I volunteered to help
set up the offering on the chancel steps. Bread had been baked
in the traditional wheatsheaf shapes and Miss Butterworth
wondered why so much had been piled so densely in one place.

"They did it like that in the Middle Ages," I said. "It gave the
impression of lots."

"Ah," Miss Butterworth smiled. "Authenticity."

The church was full by the time we had filed into the choir
stalls and yelled our way through "We plough the fields and
scatter the good seed on the land". The Forseys and their son and
his wife and children were seated prominently on the front pew.
The front of the nave had been taken over by the 'important'
people of the neighbourhood – a covey of small-time hoteliers
and guest-house proprietors, the usual dull professional types
and the retired wealthy who lived in big houses nearby as well as
a small contingent of refugee memsahibs from India.

Old Man Forsey had a deep voice and led the congregation
through the beautiful old hymns. Then the Reverend Trevor
Bunn skipped up the pulpit steps to deliver his sermon with
animated gusto more appropriate to a Punch and Judy show. It
was a demonstration of athletic Christianity unsurpassed any-
where else in Torbay. Alas the jolly young curate with his
boyish charm and crinkly brown hair did not confine his athleticism to biblical areas. The following Christmas he was
caught doing press-ups on a solicitor's wife in the vestry and
reverberations of the scandal shook the church to its found-
ations. But the faithful rallied round and Bunn – or "Hot-Arse"
Bunn as Dad called him – was replaced by a half-dead old
buzzard who had to be helped up every time he knelt.

All this was months away and the Rev. Bunn thumped out
his harvest message unaware of the cards fate would soon be
dealing him.

"Lay up the harvest of goodness in your souls," he bellowed.

"And the Lord's wain will cart you and yours gloriously up the golden road to Heaven."

During one of his long pauses Butch and I pulled the threads we had tied to the wheatsheaf loaves. They tumbled noisily to the tiles and for a moment everyone craned in that direction. The Forsey pixie was revealed amongst the thanksgiving fruit and veg. From his fishing line hung a dead mouse and he sported a coronal of sprouts on his brow. Soapy Tucker, who had been forced to Holy Communion with his parents, said afterwards it was a sort of heathen intrusion as if Puck had popped out of the Celtic past to reclaim an ancient pagan festival. The entire choir were close to hysterics for a few minutes but Bunn pressed on while the verger tiptoed away, the pixie cradled in his arms, and the congregation coughed and blew their noses. What made it so devastating was the unanimous pretence that nothing odd had happened.

Peeping through the chancel screen I saw Old Man Forsey grimly staring straight ahead with a face the colour of a pickling cabbage. Napoleon must have looked like that after Waterloo. Well, *Troja fuit* and my career as a chorister was over.

The pixie was stubbornly returned to Forsey's garden but the appearance of a large, ferocious alsatian amongst the apple trees put an end to the commando raids.

*   *   *

In October my Welsh grandfather died and Dad went to the funeral and I tried to understand Mam's grief. The horsechestnut leaves were brought rattling down by the first frosts, and blow by blow autumn attacked and captured the town. At dimpsey blackbirds shuttled noisily between Elmsleigh's privet hedges and beautiful little things belonging to the season wandered into my poetry and pictures. Nibs ran along the whitewashed wall carrying raindrops on her fur and every clear night the owl cries magicked me back to the evenings of the war. To dream by the fireside was to distil all the experiences into words and pencil strokes, and the reading helped.

I finished *The Wind in the Willows* and *The Thirty-Nine Steps* and raced through Streete's *Farmer's Glory*. Clennon was waiting at the end of the week and the prose gave me an appetite for the outdoors where autumn flared in the kestrel's plumage and the starling flocks winnowed across the water meadows.

"This Other Eden, Demi-Paradise", yes, that was it – Clennon and the sea cliffs of Down End Point and the deep Dartmoor cleaves. At the grammar school I waded through Latin and French verbs, and hacked my way through the elements of physics and chemistry, and tip-toed through the labyrinth of clause analysis. But the countryside provided a sharper reality.

Out in the wilds I saw less of Tacker. Once or twice I glimpsed him and Billy emerging from a wood or plodding up a hill, like refugees from the England of the First World War.

One Saturday morning I bumped into him on the edge of Lime Kiln Copse watching the smoke from his fire roll down the goyal. He stooped and rummaged in the embers and flicked out a couple of jacket potatoes. We ate and said nothing but I could see the age standing out in the wrinkles on his face and my heart ached for him.

"I got new ferrets," he said at last, reading my thoughts. "They idn a patch on Ladyship but they'll do."

"Midge wouldn't let me near the hutch," I said. He poked the fire with a stick and said softly:

"I know, boy. Mrs Smale told me. Midge idn sixteen ounces, you see – but I won't have 'er in no home, not my flesh and blood."

Billy whined and nuzzled my hand.

"Us'll go after they rabbits again soon, hey Bri?"

Tacker grinned. "Cor bugger! – us had some good times, me and you and the old dug."

But we were to drift even further apart as the hunting instinct withered in me and he became more of a recluse. One of my last real conversations with him happened outside the Church House Inn, Stoke Gabriel. Mam and Dad had treated me to a Sunday bus ride and were busy in the saloon bar when the old poacher brought his cider to the bench outside.

"I'll go back down the river to Waddeton and come up over to Windy Corner and home along the cliffs," he said, coughing phlegm. It was an invitation to join him.

"Doin' all right at school?" he went on, rubbing at the bleariness in his eyes.

"Pretty good, Tacker."

"Keep it up then," he said and he got to his feet.

"Still, I haven't no regrets about ort. You'm sad at the end of things, that's all. The livin' of it wadn bad even allowing for Midge."

"Mam says you'll go on forever," I said.

"Like the Thames," he grinned sadly.

I suppose the sight of me reminded him of Ladyship and made him depressed, but before very long he shrugged off his melancholia and would come whistling down Fisher Street on the way to the valley.

"The poor old bugger don't look well," Mam said.

"Could be worse," said Dad. "He could be married."

"There's nothing to stop you packing your bags and leaving, Perce."

"Never," Dad cried. "I couldn't cope with all that happiness."

And he caught her and sealed her reply under a kiss.

*   *   *

The year was turning and more fragments of the childhood world vanished with it like mice under the ploughshare wave. Yet many little things remained untouched by time – a fire of sticks and bark; a charred jacket potato; loneliness catching up with an old countryman. Schooldays blurred and faded one into the other, quickly, almost mechanically, so that a week no longer seemed endless. Nature was excluded until the final bell on Fridays and I was up and out of the house early on Saturday before Gowman's rooster had finished crowing. I had to see Bathsheba, Solomon and Edward and be with them when Ernie turned them out to grass where the spider spin glittered.

Colin and I picked up apples and bagged them ready for milling. We got ninepence an hour and worked our way through Bickford's orchards with a gang of casuals. And it was good to stop and listen to the old folk who lived in the converted railway carriages on their smallholdings. They were the last Victorians and could tell fine stories about country ways at the end of the nineteenth century. Living quietly among pullets and geese they spoke a rich dialect and whatever they planted came up strong and healthy. I would meet them again and again throughout my life in the writings of Hardy, Dickens, Tolstoy and Coppard but for me they were never mere shadows of another age.

Then the Brinhams were gone and a new cowman and his

uppity wife occupied Mill Marsh Cottage. November shrouded the valley in sea mist and the sadness I felt came from outside and had no name. During a walk over the land below the cider mill I saw Midge potato picking. The line of women in head-scarves and rubber boots made slow progress up the field. Their awkward, stooping silence was of the mist and the rattle of potatoes in the pails did not disturb it. How fat and ugly the girl had grown, and bent over her pail she reminded me of Charles Laughton as Quasimodo. But I didn't want to laugh. Her hope-lessness was awesome and I hurried on over the fields. Down from the high latitudes flew the foreign thrushes and the lovely redwings released their soft cries into the soft grey air. Miss Lee had gone and my Welsh grandad was dead and Mill Marsh Cottage was no longer a friendly place.

17
Under the Dogroses

I caught my first glimpse of her on Torre Station one wet afternoon in the New Year. She stood a little apart from the noisy gaggle of grammar school girls, her satchel under her arm and her head buried in a book. Then someone called her name – Jenny – and she swung her glance in my direction and smiled.

"She's soft on you," Colin said.

"Don't be stupid," I sneered, but the sweet sickness was busy in my stomach and for days I thought of her and nothing else.

Doreen Harris was her classmate.

"Jenny's going out with my brother," she said triumphantly. "But I'll tell her you're interested."

"Don't bother – porky."

"It's no bother. She'll die laughing, you little squirt."

I never saw Jenny Luxton and Aubrey Harris together but tortured myself picturing them hand in hand. Aubrey was a spotty twelve-year-old, very lanky and loud and self-confident. By now Aurora, who had quickly discarded Paul Quantick, was chasing me around like a cat on heat and I enjoyed it and used her to ease the misery of loving in vain. Jenny's wide, solemn grey eyes and tenderness of gaze stalked my waking moments and sank with me into sleep. I kept seeing her cropped brown hair and short, straight nose and lovely mouth and the large,

white teeth her upper lip could not quite conceal. The fine shape
of her head and her unblemished skin reduced all other girls to
faceless dolls.

Jenny was as sleek as a jill ferret. Standing under the corrugated awning of Tacker's yard, watching him push the dead
chicks into the hutches I kept trying to swallow the pain. Tacker
was acting very peculiar. He was creeping back to the dwindling
wild places, unable to cope and unwilling to fight change. Life
for him was a forest fire and he was running before it.

"Do 'ee believe in God, boy?" he asked, pressing his face
against the chicken wire.

"What sort of thing is he?" he continued immediately.
"Christ," he groaned. "Christ."

"I don't suppose he's much different from any old grown-up,
Tacker."

"Idn he all posh and straight and too good to be bliddy true?"

"It's his job – being good and that."

"Well, does 'ee get out and about with his dogs?"

"He does everything, so they say."

"But," he said turning to squint at me. "Does God keep
ferrets, Bri?"

I shrugged.

"Who knows, Tacker," and I added hastily, seeing his face
drop: "If he does everything then he must keep ferrets. Everything means everything."

"If he do," Tacker whispered. "I idn gwain object about goin'
to Hebn, no sir, only t'wouldn be proper without Ladyship."

Aurora and I went to a George Formby picture called *Let
George Do It*. Our hero played an unlikely cow-heel-pie-scoffing
secret agent liberating nazi-occupied Norway with a unique
brand of imbecile humour and a dozen long bursts on the banjo.
We sat rigidly apart pigging Hopkins's boiled sweets. The way
they clacked against her teeth made me wince. Outside words
were unnecessary and we went our separate ways through that
evening of early spring.

"Eat the liver, then, and leave the spuds," Mam said.

"I don't want it, Mam."

"Want don't come into it. Eat. It's not whalemeat – it's best
lamb's liver."

She rested her elbows on the tea table and folded her hands
under her chin and looked at me.

"Are you sickening for something?" she said.

"No Mam."

"You bloody are!" she snapped. "Are you worried about your schoolwork?"

I shook my head.

"Well, don't let it get you down, whatever it is. It's all in the mind."

Yes, I thought, everything is – you, the outside world, Jenny, God, the lot. Maybe it would be better to have less mind and keener senses, like Nibs. While Mam let fly I watched my old she cat cleaning herself on the window sill, lifting her ears everytime a blackbird alarmed or a gull spoke. Her simplicity was something to be envied.

From the carriage window yellow patches of daffodils and my facsimile gazing back at me. Then a green mist of new leaves and frothy clouds of apple blossom against the dark earth of back gardens below the railway embankment.

There were occasions after school when I failed to see her among the other girls on Torre Station but if I did spot her and got close to her she always smiled at me.

"Harris is going out with a girl from Watcombe," Colin said.

We were sitting on the Crag in Chapel Woods near the grammar school smoking tea leaves in clay bubble pipes. May had filled the trees with birdsong.

"Mary says he never went out with Jenny. He tried to but she wasn't interested."

Colin had been courting Mary Lewis for a month and knew what was going on in the lower forms of the girls' school.

"Jenny likes you, Bri – honest, no leg pull, she does."

Love sickness can numb and isolate a person and I was no exception. So Colin's words delivered casually from puffs of smoke were a glorious anthem of release. But I was down for detention the same evening and the thought of not being free to pour out my heart to Jenny while we waited for the school train ate into me throughout the long and tedious punishment hour.

I slouched morosely to Torre Station for the five-past-five and had just planted myself on one of the luggage trolleys when a low musical voice carrying the faintest of Devon accents said: "Hello."

"Hello," I said and the colour rose in my cheeks and my heart thumped. She placed her satchel between us and sat beside me.

"Mary told me you were in detention so I stayed behind for netball practice."

Jenny looked ravishing. She was a slender, brown, loose-limbed elf of a girl wearing a pale green and white striped dress with a slightly gathered waist, short sleeves and revers collar. Her ankle socks were almost as white as her teeth and her brown Clark's sandals gleamed under the Cherry Blossom polish.

During the moments before the train arrived we learnt a lot about each other. Yes, she said she'd like to see my birds' egg collection although she thought robbing songbirds' nests was cruel. No, she hadn't been to Dartmoor or ridden a shire horse or seen a snowy owl or dived off the end of Paignton Pier. But she had a bike and an old, half-blind border collie named Clem and a pet hen called Mrs McClusky and two goats called Kitty and Flora.

"My Dad's a carpenter," I said.

"Mine's a civil servant. He works in an office in Torquay."

"Have you got a posh home?"

"No – just a bungalow at Southdown Cross," she said, naming a remote, rural part of Brixham.

"Aren't you getting off here?" she added. The train was standing in Paignton Station beside the chestnuts of Queen's Park. The trees were lit by white and red candles of bloom.

"Can I come home with you, Jenny?"

"All the way? I mean – to the house?"

I nodded.

"I'd like you to," she said.

The train was moving again, following the edge of the bay, puffing past coves and beaches, over the Brunel Viaduct and on through green wooded combes full of bluebells to Churston Halt where we got out and took the single carriage connection to Brixham. Beyond the fishing port the countryside was rolling and green, edited by strong south-westerly winds. The hedges were seamed with dandelion gold. We picked bluebells for her mother and tried to flush the cuckoo that kept calling tantalizingly ahead of us. Before we reached the bungalow gate Jenny let me hold her hand and kiss her, and our lives met like two separate streams and became one clear little river holding summer's light.

The Luxton bungalow needed a coat of paint. Someone considerably lacking in imagination had christened it 'Sea Breezes' and had gone to great pains to tuck it away behind hedges of salt-browned privet. A cinder path took us round the back for a brief tour of the chicken run and the vegetable garden. Kitty and Flora Goat were eating newspapers under some crab apple trees at the bottom where the hedge was thickest. From the terrace above the rockery the view across the turf to the cliff tops and the English Channel was heat-hazed and spectacular.

Jenny left me to enjoy it and went into the kitchen. The brown and white goats wandered up to the steps and regarded me from pale eyes. Seconds later Mrs Luxton appeared at the door and I smiled up at her smooth suntanned face.

"Brian," she said briskly. "Come and have a cup of tea with us."

The flat of Mam's hand greeted me as I slunk into our kitchen. Anxiety sometimes compelled her to react violently.

"I've been selected to play cricket for the Colts," I beamed before she could mount a fresh attack.

"We had net practice after lessons. I should have told you but I forgot. Your wedding ring don't half hurt, Mam."

"Well," she panted, rubbing her knuckles. "Don't forget next time. Now go and sit down and I'll bring in your fish and chips. Burnt bloody offerings! I've been worried sick. Duw! Duw! – you'll be the death of me."

I couldn't tell her about Jenny. I knew she would be jealous and silly and make things difficult, but it was easy for us to meet secretly at the bungalow or half way between Paignton and Brixham on Galmpton Common. Quickly everything else assumed insignificance – my friends, school, games, books. Her radiance rendered the outside world dull.

* * *

Gradually Mam reclaimed her position at the centre of my world but she shared it now with someone else. Jenny was a gazelle gliding across the sunlit veldt of my dreams and if lust also sent Beryl Eccles bouncing nude out of the thicket – a veritable hippo of fleshly delight – my purest thoughts flew to Jenny. She was intelligent, generous and sincere, and also a little sad. At first I couldn't understand why. People from large families tend to assume sadness and introspection are millstones the only child is doomed to carry through life, the bequest of an enduring loneliness. They are mistaken. My Mam and Dad were a couple of overgrown kids and I was never short of companions or amusement or consideration.

We met two or three evenings a week and most Saturdays. The perfect weather of June also encouraged us to "mitch" school every once in a while. Jenny's curiosity and love of the countryside were bonuses I hadn't anticipated. So we strolled hand in hand through the deep, silvery, whispering fields and picked strawberries from under the nets against the south-facing hedge of 'Sea Breezes'.

I lived in my faded khaki shorts and cracked sandals, and carried our swimming gear and odds and ends in the canvas fishing bag. Perhaps the sweetest memory of that long hot summer is seeing Jenny at the chicken run and she with Mrs McClusky, the speckled hen, clutched to her breast, crooning a lullaby to the bird and rocking it like a baby. But then, every-thing is so close and clear although the tears spring to my eyes at the recalling of it. Mam singing "Geneviève" and tilting the watering can over her potted tomato plants; Dad scrubbing his arms at the sink and whistling; and Jenny cycling down the Old Brixham Road in a sky blue frock – blue out of the blue burning distance.

Summer can be an unbroken melody. For us it was the sea of vivid aquamarine and indigo flaked with light; and the great all-embracing liberty of childhood free of care. Goldfinches bent the cow parsley where it lifted creamy parasols to the sky, and the orange juice on her lips made each kiss delicious. O the dark byre, the dark stable and the dark barn of Cider Mill Farm. Ernie lifted Jenny up and put her behind me on the warm hard back of Bathsheba and led us up Stuggy Lane, parting the muzz of bee music and the honeysuckle scent. Jenny wrapped her arms round me and looking up through half-closed eyes I was hypno-tized by the flowing gold-fringed leaves and the rapture of her company.

These dream things do not gather dust like keep-sakes locked in a box. While we live our dreams live and the past we once trod lives. But sorrow lies in the knowledge that the past is the Forbidden Land we can walk no more. Our mistakes remain unrectified and the heartache persists. Yet age cannot intrude upon and distort the vision. Each person holds in his or her being a private sanctuary to be re-visited in reverie.

On the Saturday of Saturdays we cycled to Coleton Fishacre,

a private coastal estate a few miles south of Brixham. It was a sun-inundated day and we were glad to leave the pushbikes by the derelict shore battery bunker and walk the dusty cart track under hedges of blackthorn, may and dogrose.

The track opened onto rabbit-snipped turf that swept down to meet the bracken and the fading bluebells of Scabbacombe Head. I held her waist but mightn't have put my feelings into words if she had not suddenly turned and rested her head on my shoulder and said:

"I love being with you, Bri."

"I'd die if I couldn't be with you, Jenny."

Hidden by her hair were tiny ears like scalloped shells and to place my lips on them was ecstasy. But I would rather have put my hand in the fire than even think of touching her body.

We ran across the downs to meet the sea breeze where it lifted the coconut-scented musk of gorse and the odour of the loomeries. Here the treeless hedges were long, slender sweeps of leaf dazzle and blaze. Swifts and martins ravaged the high places leaving the bottom of the sky to the larks and gulls. Broom pods banged and a stonechat delivered its strange cry that sounded like a couple of pebbles being knocked together.

To reach Scabbacombe beach we had to drop into the Kingston Valley and follow the stream; and Jenny waded out to her knees, tucking her frock up into her knickers and splashing the water over her face and arms. Dragonflies hovered and whizzed and rattled on blue-green transparent wings and from the spinney in the throat of the coombe a woodpecker drummed.

The cows emerged from the shade of the elms and a few followed us down the stream, sailing across a big golden lake of buttercups. We ambled along and I spun Arthurian fantasies around my exploits with Tacker, guarding my tongue because the Luxtons did not use bad language. Such a discipline was easy enough considering how I worshipped her. While I acted the troubadour she made herself a chaplet of daisies and became The Lady of the Fountain. I would have trailed her mutely like a dog and lolloped off to the far corners of the world to bring her her heart's desire, whether it was Attila the Hun's favourite pony, Nero's fiddle or God's false teeth.

Kingston Brook cut a winding groove in the pebbles and lost itself in a sea of pistachio green whose wavelets were tinkling over irridescent shells. Jenny put on her swimming costume behind a rock. It was a lemon yellow delight covered with a cross-hatching of shirring elastic. Those little bubbles filled with water and pulled the costume down so that it sagged and dropped on her slippery body. But we dived and bobbed about like otters and ran back to the towels to sunbathe. Later, I climbed the cliff to the fulmar ledges, glorying in her terror, and dashed along the path to the copse on the edge of the precipice. The sun scorched my skin and the bracken fronds tickled my legs and the woodpigeons cooed from the scrub elms.

"Brian," Jenny cried. "Bri-i-i-an."

She was in the water, waving her arms, and she will always be there as long as summer returns and the sea shivers and glints over the white pebbles under the great headland.

*   *   *

"I wish we didn't have to go home," she said.

"I don't have to," I said. "I'm allowed to sleep out on shed roofs and things."

"Really?"

"Yes, I want to be like the buzzards and squirrels."

With Jenny falsehood was inconceivable. She placed a small, perfectly shaped hand in my own rough little mitt. Up the cart track we drifted, under the delicate pink blooms of the dog roses and the more robust elder flower, the honeysuckle and may, past the granite cattle trough and the nettles where the coal-tit sang. The setting sun above far off Start Point stripped us of words. We pedalled away, laughing and whooping, down the lane to Nethway and up the long hill to Raddicombe. But behind the joking and the banter was sadness that would intensify at parting.

18
Mackerel Stew

The Grammar School playing fields were at Cricketfield Road, up behind Audley Park Secondary Modern. 'Snoop' took the juniors for cricket, and the lie I had told Mam about net practice with the Colts proved prophetic. All the stone throwing and catapult contests had given me a good eye and I was able to swing a stylish bat and bowl some reasonable off-spins. But competitive cricket meant sacrificing Saturday mornings and losing precious hours with Jenny so I played myself out of the squad by dropping catches and getting a succession of ducks.

Sports Day was the major social occasion of the summer term and all the goodies brought their parents to see all the ruffians take the prizes. Boys without caps were booked for punishment and anyone caught smoking faced monstrous reprisals. I came last in the hundred yards, second in the hundred yards hurdles, second in the high jump and runner-up in the long jump. Towards the end of a golden afternoon, Hodgeson, Prout and Slocombe were caught in the groundsman's hut grouped like doctors around an animated nude fifth former from the girls' school. Ripples of the scandal spread through the ranks of delighted sprogs and the posse of masters escorting the rakes back to school received the loudest cheer of the day.

Slocombe, who later admitted carnal knowledge of the

young lady, was expelled and his cronies were suspended for a term. Colin and I marched home singing that evening. Only a few days of the school year remained before the holidays claimed us and turned us into savages again. The leafy plane trees of Grosvenor Road rustled in the wind that crept off the sea to keep the weather fine and cloudless.

*   *   *

Paignton was a bit of a hell hole in July and August. The trains queueing at the station brought half the population of Yorkshire, Lancashire and the Midlands to our beaches and everywhere was crowded. To escape to 'Sea Breezes' seemed especially delightful although Jenny liked us to meet on Paignton Seafront every so often, hungering I suppose for a quarter of a pound of din and excitement and a Pelosi icecream.

Mrs Luxton let me cut the grass that her husband neglected with a brazen idleness I hadn't encountered before. He was incapable of manual work, preferring to plant his behind in a deckchair and fondle the dog's ears and read while the bungalow fell apart and the garden became a jungle of weeds. Dad would have turned the place into a thriving smallholding but the Luxtons were gone-to-seed refugees from reality.

Jenny's father had no eyebrows and very little hair. The sun had given him the flushed, embarrassed appearance of a plucked bantam, and he would sit and sigh and groan and swig tea. The world had gone mad – Rome was in the hands of the Goths, Cheltenham and Tunbridge Wells were being looted and burned by militant trades unionists. What, for God's sake, went wrong? he'd ask Mrs Luxton, trying to bury his Devon accent under a ridiculous posh voice. And he would open the atlas and stare sadly at the countries which were still coloured pink and dream of the Empire. What on earth did we do wrong, Rosemary? – what?

Sitting beside Jenny on the steps I wondered how they would react to the spectacle of Dad standing on the table in the Friday night pub singing "Che Gelida Manina" in imaginary Italian. Mrs Luxton was too intelligent to come between me and her daughter and I'm sure she genuinely trusted Jenny, but it was obvious she hoped the relationship would be short-lived. I was, however, an enigma – I did not have what was known locally as an outrageous "Janner" accent and I wasn't stupid. Glancing up

I would catch her watching us, trying to unravel the mystery.

For all their airs and graces and the secondhand, four-seater Rover coupé standing in the garage, the Luxtons weren't happy as my Mam and Dad were happy. There was too much pretence at 'Sea Breezes' and too many quarrels broken by separate silences. Mam and Dad fought, bawled, fumed briefly and made-up like kids. They had the childlike capacity for utter forgiveness. At 'Sea Breezes' I found a bathroom, an indoor lav, a good wireless, a gramophone and a piano but there was no blood in the stones of the bungalow. Yet Jenny made it magical – the long grass and the thistles, the Toggenburgs under the crab apple trees, the conversation in the sun.

I knew no one of wide culture but we found signposts to profound things at Paignton Library, and when Mr and Mrs Luxton were out we played classical records on the gramophone. To hear Mozart's Twenty-First now is to recall summer evenings spent cranking the gramophone or kissing in the rasping silence at the end of the piece hardly noticing the tick of cockchafers against the bungalow windows.

Harbouring, perhaps, the death wish, Old Clem the dog who had not ventured from the garden for years limped out into the road one morning and was killed by a tractor. Mrs Luxton was shopping and Mr Luxton was at work, and I discovered Jenny sobbing convulsively on the back terrace. I tried to lift her wet little face to kiss but she refused to be consoled and sat hunched up in her private grief. We buried Clem under a crab apple tree and I told Jenny about God's golden halo of spirit birds and animals. Then we walked along the cliffs to Mansands, wordlessly, and I wondered if she felt intimidated as I did by all that distance. Sometimes the vastness of the universe would reach into the garden of 'Sea Breezes' and I'd feel menaced and vulnerable.

We cycled to Paignton Sands and left the bikes outside the Polsham Arms and tramped the tideline below the great steaming herd of holidaymakers.

Jenny loved Mr Stafford's Punch and Judy Show and she sat on the beach while I bought her some cockles from the shellfish stall. I hated the crowds and the American atmosphere but she had come to pet the donkeys which were carrying tots up and down the prom at a shilling a ride.

Mr "Donkey" Daniels had a purple, potato nose and the

demeanour of an Irish tinker. His donkeys were kept in a field at Goodrington, close to the Waterside Hotel where their master sat most evenings drinking cider. He was a well-known, much-loved town character who had particularly endeared himself to Dad by taking a pony onto a double-decker and asking for half fare because it was only ten years old.

The beautiful faces of the donkeys helped ease Jenny's pain. I didn't try to cheer her up for I knew she needed her grief but I couldn't understand why the masses and the noise were necessary. We stood at the entrance to the Variety Show Tent and saw a man in a dress suit hammering out a tune on the xylophone. The matinée was played to a packed house and the performer was giving it plenty of flourish and elbow but very little heart. Time swirled and dissolved and ran away like the tide.

"Clem was older than me," Jenny said. "He came to us thirteen years ago."

She let her bike fall into the hedge and looked at me sideways, birdlike and very alert.

"I knew he'd die soon," she said. "But I never thought it would be like that, not – not under a tractor."

I put my arm round her shoulders and we walked past Mill Marsh Cottage to the farm. Ernie was rubbing down Bathsheba and whispering to her in the manner of all true Wicca.

"The old lady's off her feed," he said.

"What's wrong with her, Ernie?" I asked.

"Age, that's all. She'll be all right in a day or two."

"Jenny's dog's dead," I blurted, and he listened to the story and said: "Well, at least it was quick. But," he added gently, "You miss him, don't you, lass?"

Jenny nodded, her eyes bright and full.

"And thinking of him hurts?"

She sucked in her lower lip and nodded again, and I saw the tell-tale streaks on her face.

"The hurt may last a little while, Jenny," Ernie continued. "But it'll get better. Life will fill up the emptiness."

Jenny closed her eyes and let the misery go once more in big sobs; and Ernie stroked her head and spoke to her as he spoke to the horses.

*   *   *

The heat-wave dragged on and became a drought. Pucks bog

dried up to reveal its noisesome secrets including an old safe, a typewriter, several prams and the skeleton of a pig. The police told Farmer Bickford the safe had been stolen from a London pub during the Blitz. The pig was thought to have been drowned in the floods of 1947.

"Very intelligent animals – pigs," Mr Luxton said.

Weeks of uninterrupted sunshine had ruined his nose and inflamed his chops and neck.

"They can't be that clever," I said. "Or they'd keep out of places like Pucks bog."

"Have you met Brian's parents, Jenny?" Mrs Luxton said, setting the tea tray down on top of the steps.

"O Mum – don't go on, please," Jenny said blushing. "You know what I'm like with strangers."

Mr Luxton peered over the top of his newspaper and said: "Does Mr Carter play snooker?"

"No – only darts," I said.

"Can't say it's my favourite game," he sniffed.

"Dad's a terrific gardener," I went on, and he cleared his throat and returned to the sports page.

Presently Mr and Mrs Luxton stopped sniping at me and I guessed Jenny had warned them off. But we used 'Sea Breezes' less often and spent almost every day on the beach or out in the fields.

Our wanderings carried us far along the coast from Mansands to the Dart Estuary and up the river to Totnes. And I showed her the Leighon Ponds and sat with her on Hay Tor and we ran together through the pebbles and shingle of Slapton and saw the grebes diving in the ley. Butterflies clustered the hedgerow flowers – tortoiseshells, red admirals and peacocks. Jenny picked moon daisies and herb robert and the cider apples ripened on the bough and each dimpsey swelled from a pearly haze.

South Devon was tawny, sere and raw sienna, withered and parched. The sea was so warm we could stay in the water for ages, then the "britt" or herring fry silted the shallows and immense shoals of mackerel hit the shores of Torbay and every wavelet scattered the sleek blue-green fish on the sand. As moonlight glints on choppy sea so the living stew of fish broke surface to roll and show their ocean-coloured flanks or their silver bellies. Children and adults waded among them with buckets or colanders or even zink baths punched full of holes.

We had mackerel soused, fried and smoked, but it was the catching of them that was memorable. Jenny and I were sheathed in silver scales, and there was enough laughter to bring God to his bedroom window wondering why he was wasting his time in heaven when Devon had just about the best of everything under creation.

19
Start Point

Mam let the *Picture Post* slip from her fingers, yawned, and stared sullenly at Dad. He was fumbling the screw top of his third flagon of Symond's rough cider, tongue skating across lower lip and eyes glazed above the fixed grin.

"Boozy devil," she said. "Couldn't even get out of your overalls. The apples are eating your brains, Perce, and you got bloody great bags under your eyes."

"They idn bags, Gerry," he slurred. "They're little desks for the pupils."

"You fool," she said, smiling in spite of her bad temper.

I sat trying to read the nature book that had sepia plates of foxes, badgers and wild cattle.

"Where you been all day?" Mam asked me. "You're always out and when you're home you don't speak for hours. Books, books, books – and I s'pose you'll be out again in a minute."

"Me and Col are going down the fireworks."

"Not with O'Flaherty!"

"No – not if we can help it."

"He was hanging round the steps at tea time. Just make sure you stay away from him. The little spiv set fire to Mr McCann's *News of the World* while the poor old chap was reading it. Mrs McCann nearly had a heart attack."

"That bugger's a ha-penny short of a shilling," Dad said, recalling the potato incident. "He ought to be put away."

Beaming in on the malevolence Horseshit fell out of the Elmsleigh Road plum tree and landed in front of us like a disturbed chimpanzee. We joined the throng heading through the twilight for Queen's Park.

"Should be good," Horseshit sniffed, crushing one of Colin's ears in his fist. "Got any fags, Dumbo?"

"My brother's goin' to fill you in, O'Flaherty," Colin groaned. "He reckons you're gettin' too big for your boots."

Horseshit's smile hardened into a leer and he lifted Colin up and forced him to walk on tip-toe.

"Eric ain't 'ere," he observed. "And if you squeal on me, Dumbo, I'm gonna destroy you. I'm gonna hit you like one of them Kamekaze planes – boomph!"

We scaled the wire fence and crossed the strip of wasteland to the cricket field. Along the edge of the park bordering the railway the chestnut trees were hung with spiky conkers and small children were tossing sticks up at them even though the nuts were too soft and white for any useful purpose. The firework display was a municipal farewell to summer.

"Them rockets is bloody fantastic," Horseshit said.

We sat cross-legged on the dewy grass. Across the cricket pitch the pavilion had hardened to a black silhouette and the blue of the sky was deepening to indigo. Attendants were scurrying around the display pieces.

"They let the rockets off last," Horseshit mused. "But I bet they wouldn't miss a couple."

I nudged Colin and he grinned.

"Later on we'll lift a few," the O'Flaherty pronounced, "and have our own little show."

He wasn't content to sit and admire the tableaux and pretend he was an ordinary member of the human race. He had to climb a tree as soon as it was dark and piddle on passers-by.

"How you goin' to knock off the rockets?" Colin asked.

"Like this," said Horseshit, and he slipped through the spectators, under the rope barrier and mooched up to the rocket stand. Everyone else was "oohing" as the gunpowder fizzed into a white extravaganza of patriotic fervour. "GOD SAVE KING GEORGE" swelled big and fiery out of the night. Waterfalls of brightness blazed and hiccuped and faded while O'Flaherty staggered off with three rockets almost as big as himself.

"One each," he chortled when we rendezvoused under the hedge.

"Bloody whoosh!" Colin laughed breathlessly.

"All we need now are a couple of lengths of drain pipe," I said.

"Drain pipe?" O'Flaherty sneered.

"Bazookas," I said.

"Jesus, yes," he crooned. "Bloody bazookas. Carter, you're a genius."

He tweaked Colin's ears and playfully knee'd him in the thigh, giving him a dead leg.

Several hundred tourists from the North and other foreign spots received an unexpected encore to the main event of the evening when they came milling up Elmsleigh Road en route to their digs. The rockets tore out of Mr Gowman's dismantled drainpipe and ploughed three wiggly furrows in the crowd. Then we took to Mortimer's trees and waited for the fuss to die down. 'Dangerous Attack on Holidaymakers', screamed the headlines of the *Paignton Chronicle*. 'Rockets fired into crowd cause panic in Paignton Street.'

"Whoever did it," the detective concluded, "could have blinded someone or killed a baby or something equally serious."

"Have you spoken to that O'Flaherty?" Mam said.

"Yes. According to him he was down the Olympia Amusement Arcade with Brian and Colin Yeo."

"He should be locked in a cage," Mam said, trembling with the desire to knuckle my head.

"Come on, Gerry," said Dad, "you can't blame him for everything."

"I bloody can! – he's a right little Himmler."

"And Bri's Tiny Tim, I suppose."

"He's your flesh and blood," Mam rasped, suddenly very Welsh and maternal, speaking from a pre-Norman conquest Britain. Blood ties were the highest appeal court in her life.

*   *   *

I saw Jenny on the Thursday before she was whisked off on the family holiday. The alyssums fumed honey-scented about her and I perched on the rockery of 'Sea Breezes' unable to meet her gaze. Bees hummed to the antirrhinums.

"It's only for a week, Bri," she said. Gran's expecting us."

"Rotten old Cotswolds," I said.

"Don't you love me anymore?" she said sadly.

"Yes, Jenny, yes, yes. But I don't know what I'll do without you."

We met cross-eyed in the embrace and shared double vision all through the kiss. Four seagulls slowly became two and sailed across the clifftop grass, touching wing tips and dancing on the wind.

"Sodding Cotswolds," I muttered.

The Toggenburgs advanced and bunted us gently, asking for tit-bits.

"Who'll look after them?" I added "– and Mrs McClusky?"

"My cousin Deirdre's coming to stay. She's a student nurse."

"I could come and give 'em a thing or two."

"Would you Bri?"

"And I'll put flowers on Clem's grave."

"Poor Clem."

The gulls soared and fell and flew over us. I brushed the gnats away from her face and said:

"I love you more than anything, Jenny."

"I love you, Bri."

On the way home I carved our initials on the big beech tree at Churston, high up and beyond the reach of other eyes. And the tree still stands as I write this, keeping that moment safe from time, steadfast while the world changes and leaves grow and sing and fall.

Doodlebug got into Gowman's chicken run early in the morning and killed four hens before the rooster hooked out one of the cat's eyes and ended the mayhem. Consequently the whole terrace was awake before dawn and Mrs Penk who had peeped over Gowman's back gate glimpsed the poultryman's "fancy" woman.

"Betrayed by his cock," Dad observed bawdily.

"She was in the dirty old devil's bedroom," Mam snapped. "Mrs Penk saw her standing there at the window, lifting the net as bold as brass and poor Mrs Gowman dead less than a month."

Elsie Gowman had spent the last three years of her life in a mental home and her passing had provoked little comment. But Mr Gowman had made sure his women kept low profiles and

Miss Millman who did not usually gossip confessed she had seen half a dozen different ladies enter the back gate after dark. The light from her kitchen was enough to reveal the libertines and the old lady was in the habit of sitting quietly at her bedroom window listening to the wireless.

"You can hear them laughing . . . upstairs," she told Mrs Penk.

"He buys that grubby magazine *Men Only*," Mrs Penk followed up, folding her arms and informing the covey of women who had gathered round her in their turbans and aprons.

Mr Gowman retaliated gamely and paraded his latest sex object – a red-cheeked trollope who swung down the terrace buttoned loosely in a cheap fur coat. Dad warmed to Gowman's spirit but Mam's inflexible Welsh morality was outraged and we were encouraged to miaow like toms every time the "fancy bit" passed in the catskin outfit.

"Charmin'," she'd smile and waltz by, pushing fifty but looking the right side of forty.

"What do she see in Old Man Gowman?" Mam asked.

"Pop up to his bedroom and find out," said Dad. "Have you seen the size of those underpants on his line? They could hold a prize marrow."

"He gives me the creeps," Mam shuddered. "I'd rather have a tortoise crawlin' over me."

Listening to her I felt ashamed and itchy, like I was under the bed in someone else's house while love-making was going on. Gowman's girlfriend was a potent blend of reality and illusion, a liberated lady thirty years ahead of her time. But she did not last the course. There is nothing so relentless as working class hypocrisy.

The Luxtons departed for the Cotswolds and to combat the pain of Jenny's absence I cycled to 'Sea Breezes' on Friday after tea to tread the ground she had walked upon and to feed the goats and sit on the steps watching the sea turn navy-blue. Mrs McClusky let me collect her from the coop and hold her in my arms. Soft clucking sounds crept up her throat and she gently tapped my head with her beak. O Jenny, Jenny, and the gulls blowing all over the sky and the privet hedges rocking in the wind. Her cousin was singing behind the sitting-room curtains but Jenny's bedroom was empty and the world was a dark void.

Drifts of blackberry blossom brought a touch of spring colour to the lanes, and the grogblossoms on Dad's cheeks made him look younger at night and older by day.

"The wasps will kill him," Mam said. "He's full of apple juice like a rotten windfall."

" 'Shall I compare thee to a summer's day'," Dad said, grabbing her waist and lifting her up so that her head touched the ceiling. Mam was so frail-looking and Dad's wrists were thick and strong and he handled her as I handled Nibs.

"Put me down, you idiot," she said, but the tenderness in her voice made a mockery of the words. The rainbow leapt up from the horizon beyond Berry Head and curved across the sky to fill our scullery with colour and brilliance.

*   *   *

Colin Yeo's dad was a gas-fitter and a miser. He rarely put his hand in his pocket for anything except to warm his fingers. And his money was kept in an old leather purse. For Dad this was damning proof of a mean streak.

"I'll tell you the three most impossible things in the world," he'd say. "Walking a pig on stilts up an iceberg; making an elephant's waistcoat out of fleas' foreskins; and squeezing a pint out of Ronald Yeo – the tight sod."

Mam had to give Mr Yeo half-a-crown towards the petrol when he chauffeured Colin and me to Start Point that weekend. Mr Yeo's life was a carefully calculated business venture and almost everything he undertook was profitable in typically peasant fashion. He lacked the nerve to speculate and was content to hoard small change and sniff round the jumble sales for bargains.

"Tight as a duck's arse," Dad growled.

Colin and I sat in the back of the old green van and felt alternately sick and elated all the way down through the South Hams to the Point. A stiff south-westerly was raking the sea around The Cherricks a little off-shore, and Start Bay looked dark and troubled.

"I'll pick 'ee up at dimpsey tomorrow," Mr Yeo said, helping us toss out the bed rolls and rucksacks. "Don't 'ee go near the edge of they cliffs or you'll be ridin' back to Paignton in a hearse."

We bivouacked at Pear Tree Point, under a great grey crag where the country was wild and open. A broad terrace of turf spilled onto rocks breached by spits of shingle and little inlets and channers through which the flood tide roared. Once things were laid out and the night lines were set and baited, it was fun to sit watching the massive green sausages of water fill the channers and burst white and angry. Off Lannacombe Beach waves stood up on the reef as tall and broad as double-deckers before sweeping to the shore. Into the shallows they hissed to stand up again before collapsing with a noise like muffled thunder.

"What would you like more than anything, Bri?" Colin said.

"A dog – but Mam won't let me have one."

"I'd like a boat," he said. "I'd sail her round Britain and off to the Caribbean, fishing and that."

"Why? – I mean, why do you want to leave England?"

He lifted his shoulders and let them fall and said:

"Adventures, I suppose. Foreign places are exciting."

"Nowhere's like Britain," I said passionately. "When I grow up I'm going to see golden eagles and wild cats in Scotland. I read this book by a man called Charles St John and I want to walk the big empty country he describes. Just me and my dog."

"If you're allowed to," said Colin. "A lot of those places are private."

"I couldn't live without the foxes and badgers and the green fields," I said. "I wouldn't want to live if I had to leave England."

The sun set and the driftwood fire burnt red and gold. We fried sausages in the pan and drank a brew of tea and smoked dog-end tobacco in our clay pipes. All week we had picked up cigarette butts from the pavements and gutters to make a dubious mixture called "Kerbstone Cut".

"Eric says you can catch t.b. this way," Colin said.

I nodded and drew on my pipe and spat into the fire. Start Point lighthouse sent yellow spokes swinging across the night and the tide rose again with the moon. We talked tough and tried to sound older than we were, trotting out the yarns to add inches to our stature. Colin told me he had gone all the way with Doreen Harris in her dad's allotment shed but I knew it was wishful thinking. Randy Dot had fourth year boyfriends and wouldn't squander her amazing sexuality on a novice.

Drowsiness cut the chat to the odd joke or two. We lay under our eiderdowns while the fire died and the roar of the surf grew louder, trying to stay awake for fear of missing something exciting. Far out on the ocean I saw the star cluster of a great liner, brighter than the moonlit water. My pipe was nearly out and so was I. Colin mumbled something and I remember trying to laugh. Then the moon and the lighthouse were gone and the sun was standing above the horizon as I lifted my eye-lids.

"The bloody gulls took the bait," Colin said.

He fed driftwood to the breakfast fire and kicked the empty nightlines he had piled beside the backpacks.

"All the bait?" I said.

"Every bit. One of 'em was hooked up. Serves the greedy bugger right."

"Was he dead?"

"Drowned," Colin grunted.

"I told you those channels weren't good places for nightlines, Col. The water comes in and out too quick."

"The gulls spoilt it," he said stubbornly, fingering his lower lip.

"What's that on your mouth?" I said.

"Cold sores. I get them every year. I can't put salt on my crisps because of them. They really hurt."

The wind had lost a lot of its muscle and the sea, sparkling under the early sun, looked slack and lazy. We harvested driftwood and pottered around at the camp chores. Then we swam and sunbathed and climbed Pear Tree Crag. The rock was warm and rough under my fingertips and after a while I was higher than the herring gulls and could look down on their pearly grey wings. Until that moment I had not realized gulls were so dexterous and so handsome in a liquid, silvery, ethereal way. I had taken them for granted as some people take dandelions for granted. They rose like blossom cast adrift from apple trees, totally weightless.

For a long time Colin and I sat on the top of the crag. Behind us the sheep grazed amongst the gorse and the jackdaws danced black against the turning bracken. A mesh of badger paths covered the lower slopes of Pear Tree Point but we did not see any of the animals. Sunday bloomed and died quietly, hour by hour, overwhelmed by its own serenity. Colin fished for pollack but was unlucky although I might have put a curse on the proceedings. Maybe to stand in silence close to the water, feeling the pulse of the world with his mind, was more than enough.

20
The Fading of the Magic

We sat quietly in the living room of 'Sea Breezes'. Mr and Mrs Luxton were at the cinema and Elgar's cello concerto was on the wireless. The music was a field of dark green wheat shaking with sorrow and I kept seeing lines of men in grey advancing under shellbursts across a grey landscape. Then it was over and silence looped around us.

"Your Mam sounds nice," said Jenny through the scratch and lisp of our pens.

I nodded and smiled, and she cleared her throat and said: "Why don't you take me home, Bri?"

"Dunno. Coming here's always been enough."

"Does your Mam know about me?"

"No," I said, closing my Latin exercise book.

"Why?"

"I'm afraid she'll spoil it. She wouldn't mean to, it's just that she's only used to me and my mates."

"I'm sure she'd like me, Bri. It's Christmas in a fortnight. Can't I come round then? Please – it's horrible them not knowing."

"We go up Gran's Boxing Day, Jen," I said. "Could you come to tea? Gran wouldn't mind and Mam's better when there's lots of people around. Only, it's not like 'Sea Breezes'. There's lots of joking and noise and fun."

"Dad will bring me over in the car."

The evening shuddered and the grey wave rolled and broke.

"This is good," said Mr Lockyer. He scribbled the mark in red ink on my composition.

"Why the title? – 'I Like Looking At And Listening To Trees'? Most intriguing."

I reddened and clutched the sides of my desk.

" 'Choirs of elms'; 'Hunched, psalm-singing hawthorns'; '. . . the boom and chant of beeches' – I like it immensely."

" 'I like it immensely'," Pardo mocked in the yard at lunch-time and I loosened his front teeth with a hard right cross.

Pardo came from Hele and had thick, rubbery lips and short, curly black hair. His Dad was a Co-op Insurance agent and Pardo junior had inherited a certain facility for mindless patter.

"Slum scum," he wailed, and I hit him again as prefects swarmed all over me.

"Slum scum" – bash! "Slum" – bash! – "Scum" – bash!

We weren't supposed to think too highly of Henry II but what I heard in the history lesson. had me rooting for the King. Thomas a Becket wasn't saintly. He was a pro-ecclesiastical power and corruption phoney. The common man never entered into it and I admired the four knights who put him to the sword. They were ageing, rough-and-ready cowboys doing the King's dirty work – four old hounds pulling down the yapping poodle.

"Thomas a Bucket, kicked it", I wrote.

"Knights take Bishop, check: King takes Knights, check-mate."

And Mr Kitson was not amused, but it was the end of term and ragging was acceptable.

"It reads like a *News of the World* headline, Carter," he said, smiling bleakly. "I shall frown upon this flippancy if I encounter it next year."

"You're always in the wars," Jenny grinned.

We stood in the corridor at the front of the train away from the girls' compartments and the hateful horseboxes. Grey streets and houses, the trudge of lonely old people, grey parks and gardens, grey sea and grey smoking dimpsey and the lights coming on below the embankment.

She took off her velours hat and put her arms round my neck when we kissed. Across the darkening bay Berry Head light-house winked and night crouched on the horizon.

"Do you think of me at bedtime, Jen?"

"I say a prayer for you."

"I dream about you."

"There'll never be anyone else," she said, eyes flashing as if she were daring the world to interfere.

Holly and tinsel chains lit drab winter Paignton, and we children craved the bright red berries and the silver and gold decorations. Greyness seemed to have risen like a fog. Perhaps the war had drilled the adult population into total conformity and drabness, making these things part of the urban winter like the sea mist and the grey rain and the grubby blooms of gaslight. But when Mam opened the front door the golden warmth sucked me to its heart. O the evergreen leaves, the red berries and the firelight gilding the ceiling as Nibs uncoiled from her purrs to greet me. The past lofts like woodsmoke to sting the eyes.

The dog-end of December was special then because the rest of the year seemed like a fast, a deliberate courting of austerity in clothes and outlook which ultimately lent more witchcraft to Christmas.

Tacker had another brush with the law forty-eight hours before the Christian world celebrated Jesus's birthday. He and Parry and Wilf Diamond did some serious cider drinking at Totnes market and returned to Clennon bent on mischief. They parked the van by the New Road Forest and broke into the poultry farm and acquired some premature Christmas dinners. The court case made hilarious reading in the *Paignton Chronicle*.

". . . PC Tarr opened the oven door and discovered a brace of smouldering unplucked guinea fowl.

" 'Well,' Willock cried, seizing what appeared to be a whole roast bantam and stuffing it in his mouth, 'you aren't having this one.'

"Further investigations by Paignton CID revealed that the cutlery on the table had been filched from the Supreme Fish Salon where Diamond had been temporarily employed as kitchen porter."

Tacker's age and the pathetic figure he cut before the bench saved him from prison, and probation left him unruffled.

"Lot of old twoddle over a couple of gleanies (guinea fowl) and a few bantams," he snorted.

I sat beside him on the bench under the Big Tree watching

the trucks being shunted round the goods yard.

"How's Midge?" I said.

"Her's getting worse," he grinned. "Mazed as a brush."

He closed his fist gently on Bill's muzzle and clicked his tongue. The dog gazed up at him and its tail beat against Tacker's wellies. Standing on hindlegs the lurcher licked the old man's swollen nose that was eaten into by cider acid.

Rain began to fall in fat, dark drops.

"Funny how it wadn rainin' just now," Tacker mused. "Things sort of take 'ee by surprise – doan 'em boy."

"Merry Christmas, Tacker," I said, pulling up my coat collar.

"Merry Chrismiss, ma boodie."

Tacker and Billy under the giant fir in the rain of late December, ghosts of Christmas past tugging at my heart whenever I walk past the Big Tree around the end of the year. And Billy is young again and Tacker is roaring drunk and laughing and waiting for moonrise. My hair is not grey and sadness does not drag heavily on my spirit. Behind my eyes nothing has changed.

*   *   *

The water in the drainage gut flowed clear and slow like molten barley sugar. Colin and I came out of New Road Forest adding our breath to the mist of dimpsey. From the blue smoking air the owls materialized and brought their creamy silence to the dead pine. We stood among the reeds of Dancing Fox Marsh while the delicious sensual bliss of Christmas Eve quaked in our stomachs and the owls began to call.

"I bloody love Christmas," Colin said.

He grinned and struck me lightly on the arm with his fist.

"Bliddy old owulls," I whispered, remembering Tacker's words. The reeds crackled, the stream flowed, pigeons clattered into the tops of the tall elms.

Colin followed me across the fallen tree that bridged the water. Our wellies chugged and squelched and lifted bubbles of methane gas.

Through the mist the stars glittered.

"Why don't it snow?" Colin groaned.

I could lose myself in *Pickwick Papers* where the snow lay eternally deep all over Dingley Dell.

Mam stood before the mantelpiece mirror rougeing her cheeks and pinning back her bun.

"Aren't you going out, Bri?" she murmured.

"We're going carol singing. Butch and Col are coming round at seven."

"That'll be nice," she said absently.

"You ready, Gerry?" Dad called from the kitchen.

"Give your arse a chance, Perce," Mam said, and she smiled down at me. "We won't be long, lovey – and we're only popping across the road."

I closed the book and snared by her tenderness stood up to be kissed.

"Come on," Dad said, filling the doorway with the smoke from his festive cigar. His slouch hat was pulled down over one eye and his tartan scarf was knotted at the throat. But the legs of his trousers were too long and concertina'd over his shoes.

"Humphrey Coalcart calls," Mam giggled. And they skipped off to catch the last plane out of Casablanca for the public bar of the Torbay Inn.

"My Mum and Dad and Gran are down the pub," Colin said.

"My Gran doesn't drink," I said.

"Get home do!" Butch cried. "Everybody drinks."

"Not Gran – only a port at Christmas."

Horseshit, Soapy and Barry Salter were waiting outside Penk's. We sang as we marched down Fisher Street past the pub whose doors never stopped opening and closing, up to Waterside, our torches furrowing the darkness. Butch's terrible voice soared above everyone's, clawing at the notes like a cat fighting a tin roof.

"You oughta try yodellin' under six foot of sand," said Horseshit, never totally swept off his feet by the Christmas spirit.

"You hum it and we'll soon pick it up," I giggled to Colin.

The traditional carol singing trail wound among the smallholdings and farms. O'Flaherty stopped under the ancient hawthorn at the top of Ladder Lane and sprinkled the shadows. A huge mysterious something, blacker than the darkness, rose before him breathing like a farrier's bellows.

"Jesus," O'Flaherty hissed, reeling back on his heels.

Then the "something" mooed and slithered down the bank and Colin kicked open the gate to let the cow back in the field.

"Moo-Moo scared Pale Faces," I said, holding the torch to

my chin and snarling. We were very fond of the torch-to-chin routine.

At Litstone Farm we sang "Silent Night" and collected four-and-six. Then we gave Hookhill's "The Holly and the Ivy" for half-a-crown before visiting the small fry for the tanners and bobs. Church bells peeled from Brixham all round the bay to Torquay and far inland. And it was good to sniff Christmas in the effulgent warmth that streamed from the open doors and the faces that beamed on us.

"Bickford's a tight sod," Butch said. "I vote to give his farm a miss and get back to the pubs."

"We got to go past his place," I said. "It would be daft not to sing."

"So shut yer gob, Merediff," said O'Flaherty, trusting my nose for a coin.

When we came carolling to Cider Mill Farm as tots and tackers, the sight of the animals in their homes and the sixpences and the privilege of drinking a little cider in the great kitchen had been enough. I could not bear the thought of it ending. It was good to stand in the yard that smelled of soiled bedding and root-crops while the farm cats shoulder-charged our wellies.

Once I had come expecting to see the cattle kneeling and the foxes and the badgers gathering at the stable door. The wail of the baby would hold the star low over Cider Mill Farm and the shires would stand on their hindlegs and dance. The magic had been present year after year but now it was fading. Farmer Bickford wasn't impressed by our rendering of "Little Town of Bethlehem". He had arthritis and begrudged the donation of sixpences to our cocoa tin. Yet, Santa Claus prevailed and we hurtled into the dark, cold lanes, past the empty chicken coops, under the immense black elms. Butch raced ahead, whooping and splashing through the muddy pools until his feet tangled and he did a perfect imitation of Tarzan's racing dive. This really stunned O'Flaherty who stood applauding while Butch whined and jigged up and down with pain and blew on his damaged fingers.

"You oughta be in a circus, Merediff," O'Flaherty chortled.

"You oughta be in the nut house," Butch roared.

" 'Ere," said O'Flaherty, "what happened to the peace on erf, goodwill to all men and that? Less lip or I'll really give you somefing to sing about."

The bullocks had reduced the path across the dump to a mess of wet chocolate, and there was a noisy lift and whirr-away of mallard from the flooded meadows.

"We got a goose for Christmas," said Butch, to cover his misery. "A whole bliddy goose!"

"We got a Co-op turkey," Colin said.

O'Flaherty placed torch to chin and said:

"We got a Gowman capon."

But I had seen Mrs McCann buying one of Brown's chickens and was not taken in by his braggadocio. I let the gang run on and waited for the owls to swim through the mist. Up in the neck of the wood the courting foxes started screeching and the hills threw back their cries. The winter moths fluttered round my torch and rats scurried along their runs where the garbage was mounded and covered by leafless buddleia.

"Get a move on, Bri," Colin bawled. "My feet are freezin!"

"Where we going?" I yelled, coming out of myself.

"Back to town," cried O'Flaherty. "But you can stay 'ere wiv the other rubbish for all I care."

"He's got the cash," said Barry Salter.

"Shine them torches on him quick," O'Flaherty roared.

"He's probably stuffed five bob down each sock already."

"Search his underpants for gas shillings," Colin laughed.

But Christmas Eve was special and its glory would not be denied. It was radiance and noise and comradeship and love. Humanity had come together to shout defiance under the hour glass and the scythe. Beyond the world lay infinity and loneliness no heart could endure. The stars held no love-light and love sonnets were not exchanged by the galaxies. Nobility of spirit was born of human relationships. It was a flesh and blood business of hearts enfolding hearts, and Christmas Eve was the fountain head of primitive emotions, uniting us all in the need to shed care.

Snugly around the fire at my house we drank mulled cider, cupping the warm tumblers in our hands and feeling the giddiness grow. Then, stampeding up the terrace we banged on every door and swooped into St Michael's Road to re-fuel on chips and spit scribbles at each other. A little later we were outside the Torbay Inn in Fisher Street singing "Once in Royal David's City". Dad and Mr Tucker came and stood in the porch, clutching their pint pots like the regalia of adult privilege.

When we had finished Dad said: "They want you to sing in the bar so get together quietly under the dart board and do it proper."

Unbelievably we were thrust into that beery furnace of noise and laughter. Homeric drinking was evident on all sides – the kind of drinking Brueghel would have appreciated and captured in oils. It was a straight unvarnished swilling of cider and ale with occasional whiskies or rum and blackcurrants tossed down to guarantee leglessness.

Our back street society was looser than a village and more tolerant. We constituted a neighbourhood standing on the edge of the countryside and close to it in the medieval sense. There were no moral hardcases bustling out of Women's Institutes to fart the Ten Commandments in our ears. We weren't a whist drive community centred on morris dancing and blood sports. We were working class people in a small town with chickens and pigs in our back yards and just across the No Man's Land of the allotments the whole of green and rural Devon lay like Utopia. On Christmas Eve this neighbourhood had a licence to slip religious convictions into neutral and hit the bottle.

Tacker waltzed up and patted our heads and put a bob in the cocoa tin before we could open our mouths. Even O'Flaherty was subjected to a surfeit of attention as though Christmas had transformed him from frog to boy again.

"They idn exactly angels," said Mrs Penk and Mam tried to kiss me and I had to fight her off.

"Let's have a bit of hush," Dad cried. "Give the boys a chance."

I looked up at the wall of grinning faces veiled in tobacco smoke, into the wink and flash of light on tumblers, sleevers and pint pots and the red glow of cigarettes and cigars. Surely Christmas Eve would never change. The Englishness so deeply rooted in the past and the shining simplicity would follow me into old age. One day my face would beam down on a new generation of carol singers and Bathsheba's children would plod up Stuggy Lane to the harvest fields.

We gave them 'Adeste Fideles' and Colin and I sang a show-off verse in Latin which went down very well.

" 'Silent Night'," Mam cried.

"Yes – 'Silent Night'," they all chorused.

" 'Silent night, holy night, all is calm, all is bright
round yon, virgin, mother and child. . . .' "

It did not seem odd to be singing the beautiful Christian carol in that pagan atmosphere. Certainly sentimental tears flowed but this was human nature and would always be so. Of course Dad had to join us, doing his dreadful Bing Crosby impersonation and siphoning off most of the applause. Coins rattled into the cocoa tin and the boys were dying to have a share-out. Dodging the shower of "Merry Christmases" we raced back to my house and divided the takings on the rug before the fire.

"Thirteen-and-six each!" Barry Salter gasped. "Crikey!"

We made sure he got all the small change – the farthings, half-pennies, pennies and threepenny bits.

"You'll need a sack to hump it home," O'Flaherty grinned, lighting the cigar he had lifted from Dad's top pocket.

"I never had so much money," Barry trilled.

"I'm gonna buy a pub when I grow up," said O'Flaherty.

"What you gonna do, Col?" I asked.

The chestnuts sat along the edge of the fire and saffron flickerings danced and rippled in the ceiling.

It was fine to gather in a half-circle with the light out drinking cider. We were all a little high on rapture and scrumpy – Colin, Butch, O'Flaherty, Soapy, Barry and me, swigging that strong agricultural wine while the tide of Christmas lifted us to the stars.

"I want to go in the RAF," Colin said, folding his arms round his shins and drawing his knees up under his chin.

"Bloody Brylcreem Boys," O'Flaherty grinned.

"An aeroplane mechanic," said Colin.

"The army's more fun," said Soapy. "Parachute regiment. Plenty of action."

"Dad reckons there won't be any soldiers in the next war," I said. "They'll just have planes dropping atom bombs."

O'Flaherty stared through his glass at the fire, then glanced sideways at me and gently tapped the ash off his cigar on the fender.

"Your old man's OK, Carter," he said. "He likes a laugh, don't he. Old McCann is a miserable bugger. He hates everyone under thirty and she's just as bad. It's like livin' wiv a couple of spuds."

Once freed from their shells the chestnuts were soft, waxy and shrivelled.

"Anyfing on the wireless?" O'Flaherty said.

I got the Light Programme, right in the middle of a man with a fruity voice singing about the sea in French.

"Turn it off," Soapy groaned.

"Wot was he on about anyway?" growled O'Flaherty.

"The sea – la mer," Colin said.

"Bloody daft language. Bloody frogs," said O'Flaherty. "I hate them more than I hate the Germans. Their tanks have got twenty-eight reverse gears. Yellow bastards. When I grow up I'm gonna be a professional frog killer."

"What about the pub?" I said.

"I'll kill frogs by day and run the pub at night," he sniffed.

"You're barmy," said Colin.

"Button your lip, Dumbo," O'Flaherty whispered in his low dangerous voice.

"Merry Christmas, Horseshit," said Colin, heavily sarcastic.

"Yes, well, just wotchit and pass another of them nuts."

After they had gone I sat in Dad's armchair and had another look at the card Jenny had sent me. Dawns were built around her, for she was songbird music and swelling light, a snowdrop held to the moon. But the Luxtons had guests for Christmas and she wasn't allowed out till Boxing Day. I knelt and placed another handful of chestnuts on the fire and drowsily cradled Nibs. The paper chains lifted in the heat and the cards on the mantelpiece slowly curled at the edges.

*   *   *

During the war we had spent many Christmases at Gran's but Mam had grown tired of lugging bedclothes up to Hill Park Terrace. And she was not close to Dad's brother Frank and his family of whom we saw very little. Christmas Day 1949 turned out to be a claustrophobic flop, rather like an ultra-quiet, ultra-long Sunday with gifts and mountains of edible goodies. I unwrapped the roller skates, the football shirt and an illustrated *Treasure Island* by Robert Louis Stevenson, and attacked the walnuts. Dad got up late, the ghost of last night's jollity gleaming faintly in the blood-shot hung-over cerebral murk of his eyes. After a colossal lunch and several glasses of port he slept by the fire and Mam climbed the stairs for a lie-down.

I slipped into my old clothes and ran through the deserted streets to Clennon. No one had told the farm animals it was

Christmas and they were going about their usual business. Sheep were fattening on Cider Mill Hill and the cattle were scattered over the watermeadows. The afternoon was mild and windless, and the grey sky threatened to fall as drizzle.

Ernie had let the horses out in the orchard above Bickford's farm. A buzzard cut circles on cloud and gave a thin cry. The voice of the valley, I thought, the voice of the goyals and spinneys and wooded hills. There was a softness about the landscape that was uniquely West Country: grey tracery of lichened apple boughs against a sky like a great delta of volcanic ash; a rounded hill blessed with a single oak tree; smoke lofting blue-grey from the old farmhouse; and all about me the fields at peace with themselves.

I sat on top of the five-barred gate and let my legs dangle. The shires were up among the trees on the hillside. I could hear them munching the hedgerow grass and snuffling.

"Bathsheba," I called. "Bathsheba – come on, girl."

And she blew through her nostrils and slithered down the slope to stand before me. I stroked the muscular arch of her neck, lifting her mane and drawing the strands between my fingers. She rubbed her head on the mossy gate-post and gazed at me from eyes lit by trust and contentment. A rabbit hopped out of the bank and began to feed, and a blackbird flirted its tail and chattered from the hazels. Bathsheba stirred and stamped. Looking down I saw, nestling amongst the ground ivy and brambles under the hedge, a solitary primrose; and I stared through the little yellow flower into Jenny's face. Then I wanted the fireside and the cold meat and pickles, and Dad's laughter and Mam's Welsh hymns. Tomorrow Jenny would be part of that world.

*   *   *

Unknowingly I had found Avalon. It was Yesterday and I went there as a boy and drifted through the dreaming orchards and sailed across the watermeadows where the fox danced and the barn owls called at dimpsey.

"When the snow has melted," Mam said, "all the fields will be green again."

And they were – for a little while. Now they have vanished and I see the funeral of my childhood among the housing estates and holiday camps where those long summers quivered like hallucinations.

O Jenny in your faded dress and sandals, the sun sparkling on your hair and blue summer mornings in your eyes. The larks go on singing and singing over Cider Mill Hill. Time stops flowing and I move on although the voices call me back. I have run through the dew but my footprints no longer smudge the grass.